MANCHESTER'S WATER

The Reservoirs in the Hills

TOM QUAYLE

TEMPUS

Frontispiece: *'Drought order Notification' handbill from 1901. This was distributed by hand to every household in the Manchester area. Today, we have hosepipe bans instead.*

First published 2006

Tempus Publishing Limited
The Mill, Brimscombe Port,
Stroud, Gloucestershire, GL5 2QG
www.tempus-publishing.com

British Library Cataloguing in Publication Data.
A catalogue record for this book is available from the British Library.

ISBN 0 7524 3198 6

Typesetting and origination by Tempus Publishing Limited.
Printed in Great Britain.

MANCHESTER'S WATER

The Reservoirs in the Hills

WATER SUPPLY.

NOTICE IS HEREBY GIVEN—

That, in consequence of the exceptional and long-continued DROUGHT, the supply of Water in the following Districts **will, on and after WEDNESDAY Next, the 21st inst., be Discontinued daily, between the hours of 4 in the afternoon and 8 the following morning:—**

DISLEY,
HIGH LANE,
HAZEL GROVE,
STOCKPORT GREAT MOOR,
HEAVILEY,
DAVENPORT,
BRAMHALL,
STATION ROAD, CHEADLE HULME,
ADSWOOD,
SHAW HEATH,
OFFERTON,

And portions of Higher and Middle Hillgate.

If this restriction does not result in a considerable diminution in the daily consumption of Water, it will be necessary to alternate the hours of supply.

The Committee considers it desirable that the watering of roads and streets should cease, and trusts that consumers will discontinue the **watering of gardens, swilling of flags, and washing of windows.**

As the water supply will be turned off and on **promptly** at the times stated, the Committe trust that no **unnecessary provision** will be made for the time the supply is cut off.

The Committee cannot too strongly impress upon the consumers the necessity of carefully avoiding any **Waste, Misuse, or Undue Consumption of Water,** and they rely upon their co-operation and assistance in this matter.

THOMAS MOLYNEUX,
Waterworks Engineer.

St. Peter's Square, Stockport,
August 20th, 1901.

Connell & Bailey, Printers and Bookbinders, St. Peter's Square, Stockport

Handbill Dated 1901 - Drought Order Notification.

Distributed By Hand To Every Householder Living In Areas Of Manchester. Today We Have Hose Pipe Bans Instead.

Contents

Acknowledgements

To my close friend of over twenty years, Willy Russell, without whose friendship, encouragement and support this book would never have been written.

To United Utilities for their assistance, co-operation and supply of updated material, particularly to their staff, Gary Wright and Ian Allwood, stationed at Longdendale.

Finally to my publishers, Tempus Publishing Ltd, for their faith in me – on the dry subject of water.

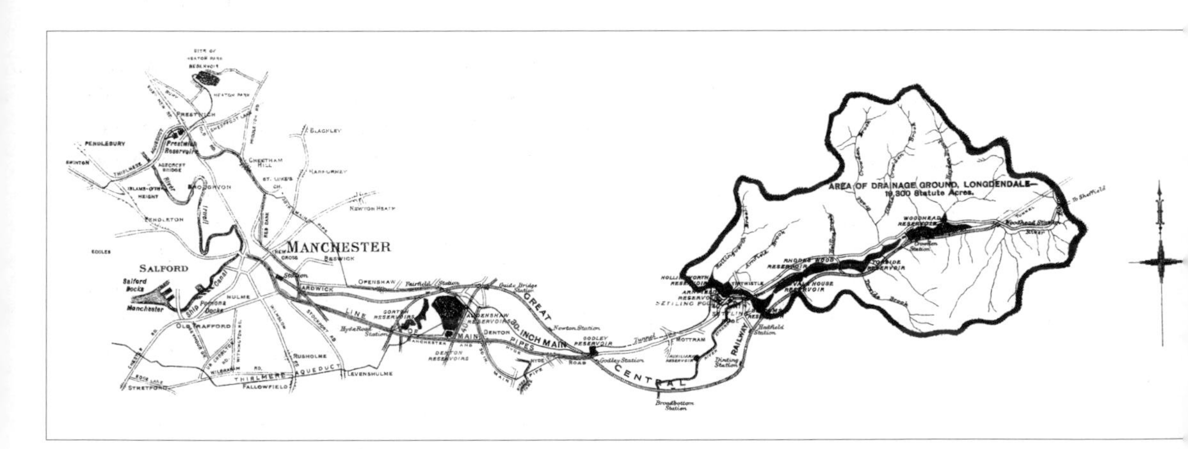

Plan showing the location of reservoirs.

Introduction

The beauty of the Longdendale Valley, set in the Derbyshire Peaks, is undoubtedly enhanced by its chain of reservoirs – vast areas of water – and this water is used to supply the needs of some 1.5 million people in Manchester, Salford and other neighbouring towns. The story behind the project is fascinating – so much so that the opportunity to publish this illustrated description and history was welcomed with open arms. We hope you will enjoy the outcome.

The Longdendale catchment has an average annual rainfall of 52 ½ in with a catchment area of thirty sq. miles, and although the reservoirs were designed to have a total holding capacity of 4,200 million gallons of water, due to the silting up of the reservoirs, the present holding capacity is some 3,800 million gallons.

The five principal reservoirs in the main Longdendale Valley were constructed on the original course of the River Etherow; Woodhead, Torside and Rhodeswood for drinking water, and Vale House and Bottoms to provide compensation water to the River Etherow. Two smaller reservoirs, Hollingworth and Arnfield, were built to be used in conjunction with the chain in the main valley.

The reservoirs were, at that time, the largest chain of reservoirs to be constructed in the world. Manchester and Salford's first major water supply became Europe's first major Water Conservation Scheme – no idle boast, but a claim richly deserved by the city fathers of Manchester, who in 1846 openly deplored the fact that in Manchester and Salford less than a quarter of homes had a tap in their own sink. The majority of people shared a tap in the street or squalid court where they lived, and even then the water supply, often contaminated, would only be on for a short period each day.

Imagine the inconvenience, but more importantly, think of the immense health problems. For less than £4, we turn on the tap and without further thought have an abundant supply of pure, clear sparkling water – and included in the price is the cost of our sewage disposal. On average, each of us uses about 27 gallons (125 litres) of water per day for drinking, washing, cooking and cleaning. Every time we go to the loo, each flush carries off 2 gallons (9 litres) of water, and our washing machines uses 25 gallons (114 litres). Water comes from the heavens; let's treat it with respect and never waste it. Of the 24 million gallons of drinking water that go hurtling towards the city of Manchester each day, almost 6.6 million gallons are consumed by the thousands of people living in the Hyde and Denton area, who still rely solely on the Longdendale Valley water.

Today, much is made of the North *v.* South divide. We in the North West, originally due to the quest for water power by the mill owners to drive their machinery, can be proud to be called the pioneers of water for the millions.

Notable dates during the constructional period

Description	Commenced	Completed
Woodhead Reservoir	August 1848	February 1877
Mottram Tunnel	August 1848	October 1850
Rhodeswood Reservoir	April 1849	June 1855
Torside Reservoir	April 1849	July 1864
Arnfield Reservoir	May 1849	March 1854
Hollingworth Reservoir	May 1849	March 1854
Vale House Reservoir	July 1865	July 1869
Bottoms Reservoir	November 1867	February 1877

Storage reservoir data

Name of reservoir	Area	Capacity	Depth	Height of top water level above ordnance datum	
	Acres	Gallons	Feet	Feet	In.
WOODHEAD	135	1,181,000,000	71	782	0
TORSIDE	160	1,474,000,000	84	651	3
RHODESWOOD	54	500,000,000	68	574	6
VALE HOUSE	63	343,000,000	40	503	0
BOTTOMS	50	407,000,000	48	486	0
ARNFIELD	39	209,000,000	52	540	3
HOLLINGWORTH	13	73,000,000	52	554	9
GODLEY	15	61,000,000	21	478	0
Service reservoirs supplied from the storage reservoirs					
DENTON, No.1	7	30,000,000	20	321	6
DENTON, No.2	6	23,000,000	20	321	6
AUDENSHAW, No.1	80	528,000,000	27 ½	340	0
AUDENSHAW, No.2	69	371,000,000	22 ½	323	0
AUDENSHAW, No.3	102	542,000,000	22 ½	323	0
GORTON, UPPER	34	123,000,000	26	259	0
GORTON, LOWER	23	100,000,000	29	244	0
PRESTWICH	4½	20,000,000	22	347	0
TOTAL	854½	5,985,000,000			

J.F. Bateman

The man who designed and constructed the reservoirs at Longdendale

John Frederick Bateman was born at Lower Wyke, near Halifax, on 30 May 1810, and was the eldest son of Mr John Bateman, of Ockbrook, Derbyshire, and his wife Mary Agnes La Trobe, daughter of the Revd. Benjamin La Trobe, a former well-known Moravian minister at Fairfield, Ashton-under-Lyne. His mother was descended from an old noble French refugee family and he assumed that name by royal licence in 1883. He was educated at the Moravian schools of Oakbrook and Fairfield. He was apprenticed to Mr Dunn of Oldham, a surveyor and mining and civil engineer. In 1834 he lived in Pall Mall, Manchester, and commenced business as a civil engineer and surveyor.

For many years, his business address was Brown Street, and he resided at the Polygon, Ardwick. In 1841 he married Anne, the only daughter of Sir William Fairbairn; they had three sons and four daughters. In 1859 he purchased the estate of Moore Park, Farnham, where his later years were spent.

In 1860 he was elected a Fellow of the Royal Society, and in 1862 he became a member of the Athenaeum Club. He was a Justice of the Peace and Deputy Lieutenant of Surrey, and in 1866 was appointed Sheriff of the County. In 1878 and 1879, he was president of the Institution of Civil Engineers.

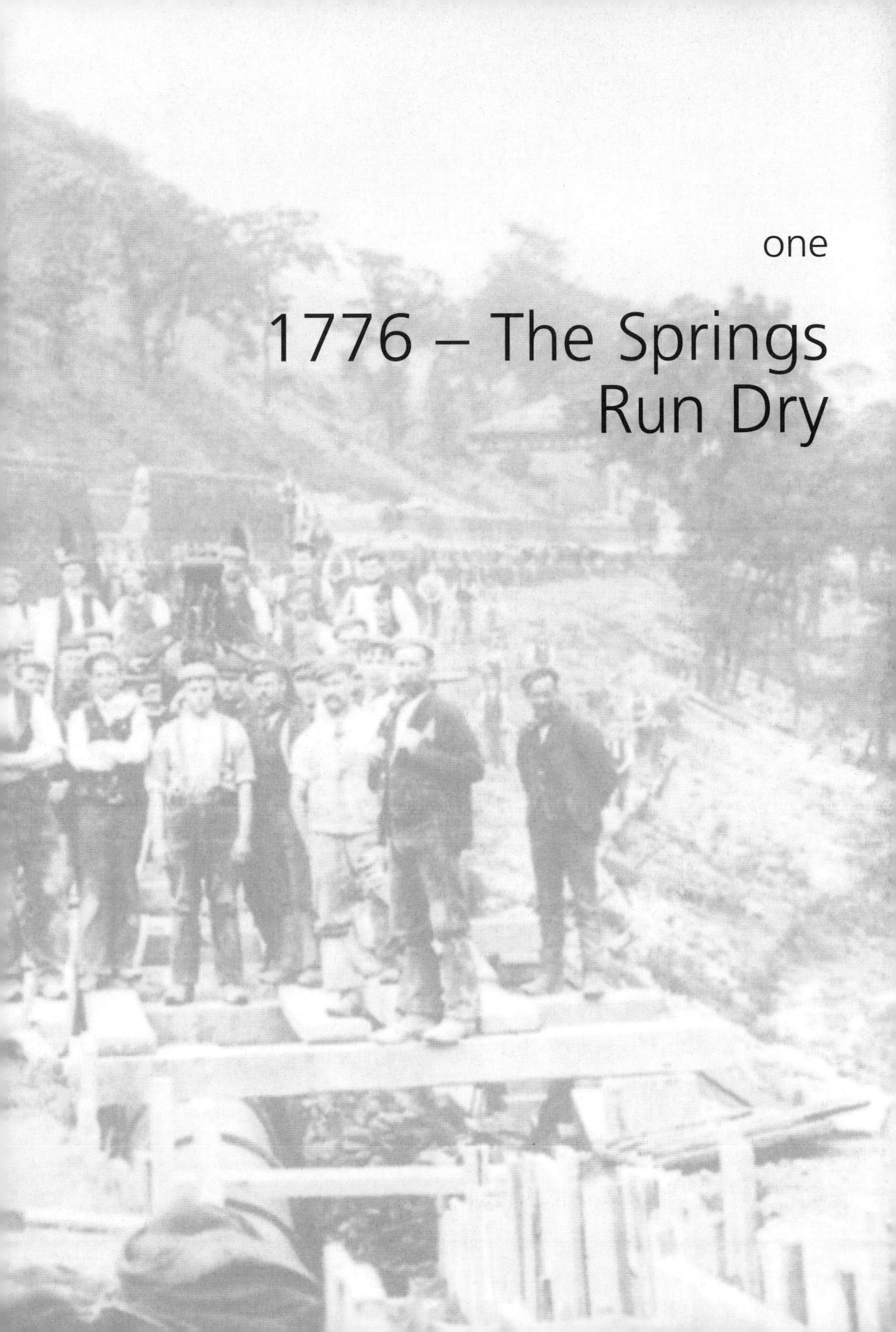

one

1776 – The Springs Run Dry

The Sixteenth and Seventeenth Centuries

During the greater part of the sixteenth and seventeenth centuries, water supplies for the large towns were obtained from water butts, wells, springs, or from polluted streams and rivers. Even rainwater was so blackened by soot that it was described as being as black as ink, and was useless until it had time to settle; many town dwellers had to pay water-carriers or buy from water-carts.

The great town of Manchester boasted a public water supply from as far back as the year 1506, the chief source being from a spring or fountain rising in what is now the bustling city centre, and from which the name 'Fountain Street' is derived. The water was conveyed by wooden pipes and open conduit for the half mile or so to Market Place, in the Victoria Street/Shambles area, close by the Cathedral.

The fascinating records of the Court Leet reveal that because this water was being sought after by a wider area of population, in 1578 the Leet Jury limited the daily ration per household to 'no more than could be contained in a vessel that one woman was able to carry on her head'.

Eight years later, a Keeper was appointed to protect the conduit from the vandals of the day, and in 1626, the Jury banned 'the washing or cleansing of calves' heads, meat, linen or woollen clothes in the open part of the conduit on penalty of a fine of twelve pence'.

It is recorded that at the coronation of Charles II, on 23 April 1661, the civic dignitaries and officials marched through the town, 'and drank His Majesty's health in claret, running forth at three streams at once of the said conduit'.

In 1776 the precious water was in so much demand that the springs were no longer able to cope, and then, due to repairs being neglected, the conduit collapsed.

Water supplies were then procured from wells sunk into the hard red sandstone, but the water from these wells was often hard and impure, and alleged by the medical authority to be injurious to health.

The Eighteenth and Nineteenth Centuries

Towards the end of the eighteenth century, the Lord of the Manor, Sir Oswald Mosley, established a pumping engine by the river Medlock. This water was pumped into small reservoirs at Halt Town, Beswick, about one and a half miles from the existing Town Hall, from where it was delivered through wood and stone pipes to other parts of town.

The greatest fraud in waterworks history was perpetrated in 1808, when the Stone Pipe Co., whose members were all non-residents of Manchester, were granted the powers to form the Manchester & Salford Waterworks Co. The chief purpose of the Stone Pipe Co. in securing control of the water undertaking was to enable them to sell to the waterworks company pipes, cut out of solid stone, under a patent granted to one of the proprietors of the Stone Pipe Co. Sixty miles of pipework, to the value of £36,984, were purchased and laid in the ground with few being connected to the water supply, and most of the pipes that were connected to the supply were defective and incapable of withstanding the water pressure.

The Stone Pipe Co. made vast profits, and then as a final slice of fraudulence, they sold to the waterworks company, for the princely sum of £14,000, 'the whole of their rights, title and interest in and to the ancient waterworks at Manchester'.

When the deception was discovered and all payments had been made to the Stone Pipe Co., they went into voluntary liquidation and resigned as members of the Manchester & Salford Waterworks Co.

The 'Market Place' area, 1823.

It is incredible that not one of the Directors who were responsible for this nefarious conspiracy to defraud were ever brought to trial. The unfortunate Mancunians had to foot the bill for the complete re-laying of pipes with cast iron, a material at that time considerably cheaper than stone.

Private enterprise continued in the hands of men who were residents of Manchester, who took immediate action to obtain a purer and more adequate supply of water. Their immediate response was to obtain water from outside the township from streams which were comparatively free from pollution.

By 1823, larger reservoirs were constructed on high ground at Gorton, almost four miles from Manchester and Salford, and which at that time had a population of approximately 200,000 persons.

It should be remembered that the loose-surfaced macadamised roads of the nineteenth century were very dusty because of the horse-drawn vehicles using them, thus creating a health hazard from the powdered horse dung which was breathed in by all road users. The Borough had many complaints about the inefficient watering of the streets, and so in 1825 a special pipeline from the town's yard to St Anne's Square was laid to improve the situation.

The firemen of the day considered themselves lucky to have sufficient water to fight a fire, even with their hand-operated pumping engine. By 1840 the water supply was still inadequate, for the waterworks company supplied less than a quarter of the houses in the Borough. One

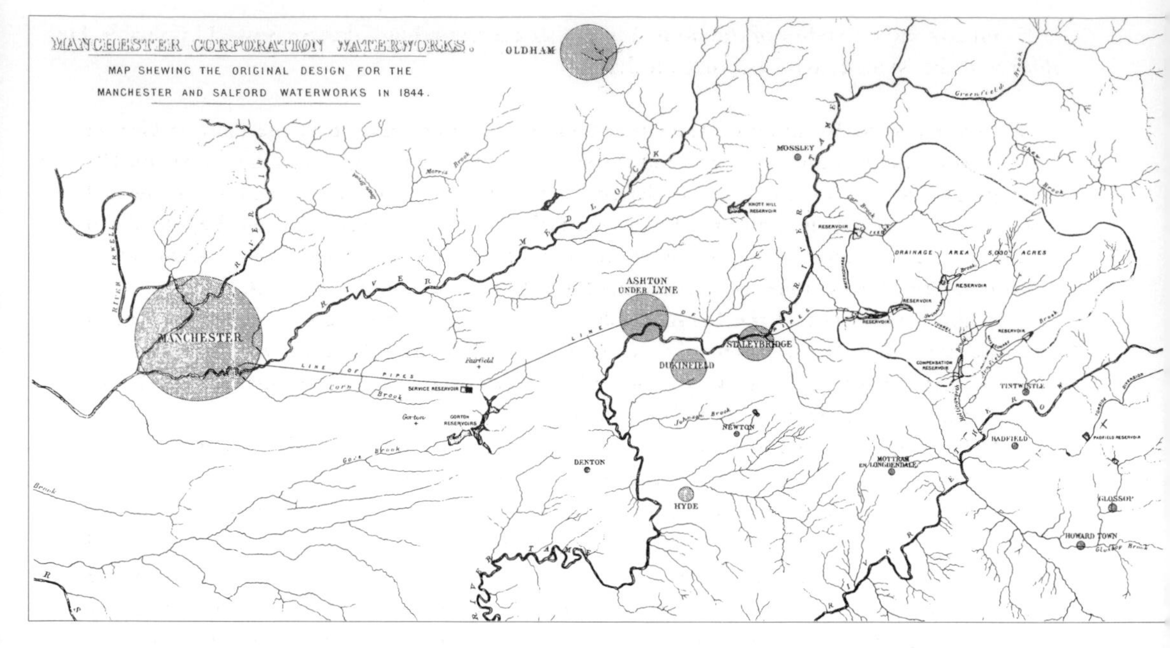

Map showing the original design for the Manchester and Salford waterworks in 1844.

water-closet would have to serve ten houses, and each household paid half-a-crown per year for its supply.

A new line of 24in-diameter pipes was laid from Gorton Reservoirs along the Hyde Road to Manchester, with a network of pipes to supply the nearby villages and farms. A further supply was augmented by water drawn from the Manchester & Stockport Canal, and two more wells 12ft (3.66m) in diameter and sunk to a depth of 212ft (64.62m) were later constructed at the Gorton Reservoirs.

These wells and the pumping engines used for extracting water were the last improvements carried out by the Manchester & Salford Waterworks Co., who had never provided a satisfactory service.

Meanwhile, fourteen miles away, the small town of Glossop was becoming prosperous, and was reputed to have 56 mills out of the 112 in Derbyshire. Fifty gentlemen, known as the Glossop Commissioners and comprising mainly mill owners intent upon protecting their own interests, obtained an Act of Parliament in 1837, empowering them to construct the Glossop Reservoirs. This was for the purpose of impounding water and regulating the flow to power the machinery for their mills. The Hurst Reservoir was the first to be constructed, in 1838; the engineer was Thomas Ashworth and his surveyor was a young man by the name of John Frederick Bateman.

In 1844, as a result of the report of the Commission of Inquiry into the Health of Large Towns, water supply assumed greater significance, and in 1846, Manchester Corporation, having come to the conclusion that the supply of water was a matter for the municipality, promoted a Bill to acquire the works of the Manchester & Salford Waterworks Co. This resulted in an invitation being accepted by the same John Frederick Bateman, to advise them on the best means of obtaining an additional supply of water for Manchester and its neighbourhood.

Bateman's earlier studies of the rainfall in the area surrounding Glossop proved invaluable. He informed the Manchester Corporation that:

> Within ten or twelve miles of Manchester, and six or seven miles from the existing Gorton Reservoirs, there is this tract of mountain land abounding with springs of the purest quality. Its physical and geological features offer such peculiar facilities for the collection, storage and supply of water for the use of the towns and plains below, that I am surprised they should so long have been overlooked. There is no other district within reasonable limits, nor any other source from whence water may be obtained which will bear comparison with it.
>
> In the highest part of the Pennine Chain, the River Etherow and its various mountain tributaries take their rise. Some of these uniting near Woodhead form there a deep romantic valley called Longdendale, running for several miles nearly due west. The summit of this district is Holme Moss, nearly 2,000 feet above the sea.
>
> The valley is hemmed in to the west by the high land at Mottram, which, however, is not high enough to intercept the clouds driven before the westerly winds.
>
> The clouds thus stopped will become embayed in the deep ravines and trough-like valleys which lie behind these summits, from whence they can scarcely escape until they have deposited their contents. The quantity of rain in the locality will therefore, be unusually abundant, while the absence of this flat land on the tops, and the steep declivities of the sides will cause a very large proportion to run rapidly off in useless floods and torrents. The water thus flowing from the surface, and which may be collected in reservoirs constructed for the purpose, will be as nearly as pure as it comes from the heavens.

Thus, John Frederick Bateman – pioneer, water engineer extraordinary – delineated his plans and submitted his great scheme for supplying water from the Longdendale Valley to the ever-growing town of Manchester.

The realisation that there was a need to provide the population with unpolluted water supplies had begun, and with it came the birth of the bustling water industry. This was the age when water-wheels provided the power to drive the machines in the mills and factories, and when water was in demand to supply dyeworks, processing plants, printworks and railways.

The rich and powerful mill owners, busily making their fortunes in the line of mills along the banks of the river Etherow, strenuously opposed Bateman's plans for constructing reservoirs – reservoirs which at that time would be not only the largest chain built stepped one upon the other on any river in the United Kingdom, but the largest in the world.

Engineers and surveyors were enlisted from far and wide. More than 1,000 navvies, miners and stonemasons, many of them lowly paid for their endeavours, hurried to the village of Tintwistle to be employed. They joined their chief engineer Mr Bateman, who was to become the greatest dam-builder of his generation.

They fought the elements, using picks and shovels, carts and horses, steam engines and crude machinery. They sank shafts through shifting sands, bored through rock to form tunnels, and moved thousands of tons of earth and clay before they finally achieved and completed their man-made lakes.

Through his handwritten reports, John Frederick Bateman unfolds his own story, fresh from his mind as he diligently informed his Manchester Corporation Waterworks Committee of problems and solutions. We share his successes, disappointments, and his difficulties, which he tempered with frankness, as he struggled to construct earthen dams to impound the often turbulent waters of the river Etherow.

Waterwheels in a typical Cotton Mill, 1827. The wheel in the background is 25ft in diameter and 18ft wide, developing 80hp. The wheel in the foreground is 21ft in diameter and 7ft wide, developing 30hp. The mill originally belonged to Richard Arkwright.

Bottoms Quarry, Tintwistle, c.1895. The men wearing leather aprons probably denote the 'Master Stonemasons'. The steam engine is visible in the background.

Almost forty years later, in 1884, Bateman published an impressive leather-bound book entitled *The History and Description of The Manchester Waterworks*, by John Frederick La Trobe Bateman, FRSS, CE, RGS, and so on, for by now he had added his mother's maiden name, La Trobe.

His Waterworks Committee Reports are signed 'J.F. Bateman', the name by which he is referred to throughout this book. Bateman's original handwritten reports were also bound into three leather-backed volumes from whence much of the material for this book was extracted.

Bateman's first report, from Volume 1, reads:

Manchester 14th October 1846

To The Town Clerk,

My Dear Sir,

Manchester Waterworks

According to promise, I give you a short outline of the project for supplying the town with water.

The quantity of water now required for the complete supply of the inhabitants of Manchester and Salford and their suburbs may be taken at about 8,000,000 gallons of water per day and at the rate of which the town is increasing it may be anticipated that the demand will be doubled in the course of the next twenty years.

It is therefore prudent to lay out the work with a view to this extent of supply and that they should also be adapted to subsequent extension to meet the wants of future periods.

I have endeavoured to keep these objects in view and so to arrange the scheme that while the immediate wants of the town may be supplied at as cheap a rate as an equal quantity of water can from any quarter be obtained, the works necessary for this purpose should still form parts of a greater scheme to be carried out step by step as the demand increases.

The gross cost of the works including the purchase of water rights and compensation to Mill owners, to bring 20,000,000 gallons of water to Manchester per day may be; taken at £200,000. To bring 8 to 10,000,000 gallons per day would require an outlay of about £140,000 or £150,000 including the full compensation for the entire scheme to the Mill owners.

This is all that need in the first instance be expanded, although the Parliamentary plans must include the whole.

In the present stage of proceedings this description will probably be sufficient for your purpose. In a few weeks everything will be prepared in detail.

I am dear Sir,
Very truly yours,
(signed) J.F. Bateman

P.S. The above estimates are exclusive of the cost of distribution in the Town.

Certain preliminaries had to be observed before a Bill could be presented to Parliament. Under the Preliminary Inquiries Act, a Court of Enquiry was convened, consisting of four surveying officers, one of whom was George Rennie. (He was the son of the famous civil engineer, John Rennie, who designed both the Waterloo Bridge and London Bridge).

Their first meeting was held at Manchester Town Hall on 26 January 1847, and their recommendations were made known on 3 March 1847.

On the subject of pollution the surveying officers reported:

> The insufficiency of the present supply is evident, and the usual consequences attendent upon such insufficiency are found among the poorer population. Some drink of wells which are polluted by leakage from the sewers and by drainage from grave yards; others obtain a scanty supply by buying from persons who carry water about for sale; some even take for domestic purposes the putrid waters of the canal or River Medlock, which used as they are, the latter as a drainage for the sewers, and both for the grosser purposes of the, factories are almost too noisome to be approached. In some parts we find the neighbourhood flocking to catch the water which flows from the condensed water pipe of a steam engine and often very undesirable contentious result.

They commented favourably on the Longdendale water and said, 'they were the purest waters they had ever seen, and that they exceeded even those of the Cumberland Lakes'.

The surveying officers concluded by recommending the Manchester Corporation to proceed with their Bill to Parliament, which prompted Bateman to write his second report:

27 July 1847

> Corporation Waterworks
>
> The bill as it has passed through Parliament and received the Royal Assent (9th July 1847) has not been materially altered from the shape in which it was introduced – but the opposition of the Mill owners having been withdrawn on the understanding that application should be made to Parliament in the next session for powers to construct further works and give them a larger guaranteed quantity of water as Compensation.

Wood and stone water pipes. Today, the new pipes are mainly cement-lined cast-iron ones. Old unlined pipes become encrusted with rust and inhibit the flow of water. They have to be scraped out and relined with cement to alleviate this problem.

ANNO DECIMO & UNDECIMO

VICTORIÆ REGINÆ.

****

Cap. cciii.

An Act to enable the Mayor, Aldermen, and Burgesses of the Borough of *Manchester* in the County of *Lancaster* to construct Waterworks for supplying the said Borough and several Places on the Line of the said intended Works with Water, and for other Purposes. [9th *July* 1847.]

WHEREAS an Act was passed in the Forty-ninth Year of the Reign of His Majesty King *George* the Third, intituled *An Act for more effectually supplying with Water the Inhabitants of the Towns of* Manchester *and* Salford *in the Parish of* Manchester *in the County Palatine of* Lancaster, and certain Persons were thereby incorporated by the Name of "The Company of Proprietors of the *Manchester and Salford* Waterworks:" And whereas another Act was passed in the Fifty-third Year of the Reign of His Majesty King *George* the Third, intituled *An Act for enlarging the Powers of an Act of His present Majesty, for supplying with Water the Towns of* Manchester *and* Salford *in the County Palatine of* Lancaster: And whereas another Act was passed in the Fifty-sixth Year of the Reign of His Majesty King *George* the Third, intituled *An Act for alter-*

49

53

56

[*Local.*] 30 *G*

Act of Parliament, 9 July 1847.

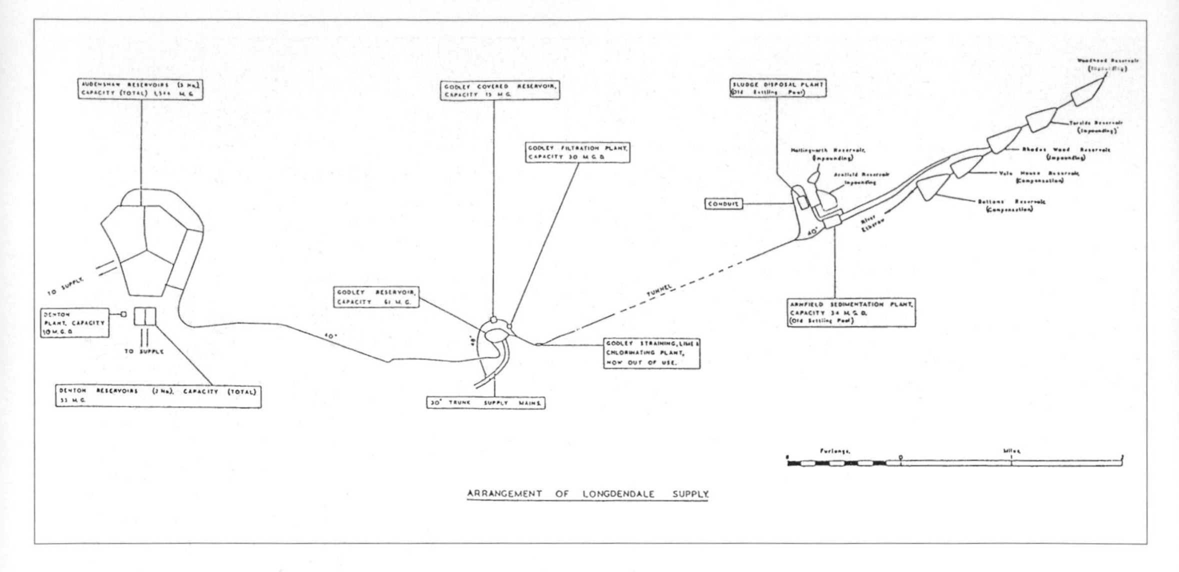

A modern arrangement showing the route taken by 'raw' water collected in the chain of reservoirs before receiving full treatment and going into domestic supply.

The Water Authority still has to pay into the river Etherow 10 million gallons of water per day to compensate for the dams being constructed across the original river bed and thus stopping the natural flow of water which supplied the mills with water and water power.

The several mill owners who Bateman referred to in his report as having temporarily withdrawn their opposition on the understanding that their Compensation Water would be increased at the next session of Parliament were the Vale House Mills, the Tintwistle Mill, Bottom's Lodge Mill, Waterside Mills, Best Hill Mills, Broadbottom Mills and the Hodge Printworks.

Bateman had successfully crossed his first hurdle. The Manchester Corporation Waterworks Act of 1847 was passed by Parliament and included the purchase of the existing works of the Manchester and Salford Water Co.

The Bill gave the Manchester Corporation the right to construct the following works:

1 Woodhead Reservoir
2 A spring watercourse to convey drinking water from Woodhead to Arnfield
3 Arnfield Reservoir and Hollingworth Reservoir
4 A masonry aqueduct to convey drinking water from Arnfield and Hollingworth Reservoirs to a service reservoir at Godley.

The mill owners also insisted that the compensation-gauge which was to be built in the first instance immediately up-stream of the Vale House Mill (this mill being the highest up the river) would be removed on completion of the final scheme, and a new water compensation-gauge constructed immediately downstream of the completed works.

The mill owners would also be entitled to be paid compensation for their mills and properties which might be submerged by the construction of the new reservoirs.

A year later an additional Act of Parliament went through unopposed, and received the Royal Assent, dated 22 July 1848, which included the following:

Rhodeswood Millowners Gauging Basin. On completion of Bottoms Reservoir, the gauging basin was removed to Bottoms. (See explanation of a gauging basin on page 86).

Rhodeswood river diversion – waste watercourse and stop gauge. In times of low rainfall, the water would normally flow through the Millowners Gauging Basin, then to the river, but during or after a period of prolonged rainfall, the sluice-valves, as shown in the picture, would be opened to allow the flood or excess water to escape via the waste watercourse and flow into the river.

Navvies laying the 40in-diameter cast-iron main from Rhodeswood to Arnfield.

1. To enlarge the Woodhead Reservoir, by raising the embankment (dam) by 6ft (1.83m). This would then increase the yield of water from the reservoir and would enable it to be utilised in two ways:

   a) for the storage of turbid or discoloured water, which could then be released as compensation water to the river below; and

   b) when the water was sufficiently clarified, it could be conveyed to Manchester via the watercourse and aqueduct to be used as drinking water.

2. The construction of Torside Reservoir

3. The construction of Rhodeswood Reservoir

4. The construction of a masonry lined flood-watercourse between Woodhead and Rhodeswood Reservoirs and an aqueduct to convey water between Rhodeswood and Arnfield Reservoirs.

In the face of all opposition, Bateman had scored a victory over his adversaries. He must have had great satisfaction in recalling the following anecdote:

On being cross-examined as to the character of the water, especially as to water which issued from peat or peat-coloured ground, I had stated to the following effect, 'that the streams in dry weather were very small and particularly clear and pellucid – walking over the hills wherever I had found water a vamp or peat bog discoloured or tasting of peat, I had found, by following the stream as it flowed, that it invariably lost all taste and colour within half-a-mile or so of the place at which it escaped from a stagnant swamp; whether this was by admixture with spring water in its course or by exposure to the atmosphere in a running stream, I did not pretend to say, but it was a fact which I had repeatedly observed, and which anyone might go to the hills and observe for himself.

Two zealous gentlemen, in their eagerness to ascertain whether an assertion I had made in my evidence as the result of frequent observation was true or not took to the hills while the inquiry was going on, and were overtaken by a snowstorm, in which they had lost their way and nearly perished from cold and exposure. Long after dark, after wandering about the whole day, they accidentally fell or stumbled into a sort of cave at the Seal Bark rocks, at the head of the Greenfield Valley in Saddleworth, which afforded them some protection from the biting winds and storm. The thermometer that night fell to 13° Fahr. in Manchester, and must have been not far from zero in the elevated region in which they were exposed. They were happily enabled to keep each other awake during the night, and shortly after leaving their retreat at daybreak the next morning, they discovered where they were, and were fortunate enough to reach a place of safety without further injury than frost-bitten toes and fingers.

In his *History of The Manchester Corporation Water Works*, Bateman describes his original design of the Mottram Tunnel (as shown above) and Woodhead Reservoir, including the service reservoirs at Godley and Denton.

Concrete tube carrying spring water across the flood watercourse, during its construction at Arnfield Reservior.

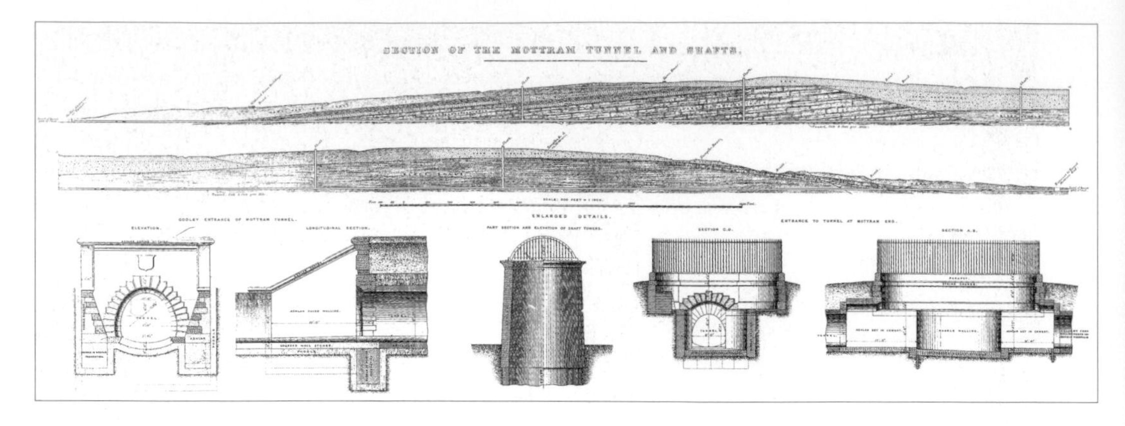

Section of the Mottram tunnel and shafts. Although the deepest of the five air-shafts is 200ft, the top of the air-shafts protrude only 15ft above ground level. One such shaft can be seen on the left-hand side of the M67, near Mottram, when travelling from the direction of Hyde.

Mottram Tunnel

This tunnel pierces the ridge which lies between the valley of the Etherow and the valley of the Tame. No water could be conveyed to Manchester till it was completed. It is around 3,100 yards in length and, like most of the watercourses in connection with it, has a fall of 5ft in a mile. It was at first intended to be 5ft in diameter, and equal to the passage of 36,500,000 gallons of water per day. It was constructed to be 6ft in diameter, and is capable of passing upwards of 50,000,000 gallons per day. This ridge had never previously been pierced, but it was well-known that between one end and the other, a great fault or dislocation existed. Before the work commenced, borings were made along the line of tunnel to ascertain the character of the material through which it would have to be driven. These borings disclosed the existence of a bed of quick-sand and silt, upwards of 80ft in depth, and extending about 700 yards over the centre of the tunnel.

Beneath this quick-sand to the bottom of the tunnel, there lay a bed of black shale, 50 to 80ft thick. When this shale was reached by the preliminary borings, a large quantity of water rose to the surface. Pipes of a 2in diameter were reared perpendicularly above the surface of the ground, together 18ft long, and from the top of these the water poured, throwing up stones as large as pigeon-eggs, some so large and angular that you wondered how they could rise from such a depth through a 2in bore-hole and be thrown about by the pressure of the water onto the surface of the ground.

It was, therefore, comprehended that in this quick-sand a large quantity of water would be met with, and the positions of the shafts were arranged so as to avoid it. The work was let to Mr Graham in August 1848.

On emerging from the Mottram Tunnel, the water is carried across a small brook for a short distance by an inverted syphon pipe, and then, for a short distance also, by a covered culvert to the Godley Reservoir. This reservoir is on the slope of the hills and is the last point at which a reservoir of suitable elevation could be constructed. It is formed partly by excavation and partly by embankments, out of the drift or boulder clay, which here, as in other places, rests upon a bed of fine sand. This sand made its appearance in various places within the basin of the reservoir, and had to be covered by clay tied into the surrounding retentive material.

The elevation of this reservoir when full is 328ft above Piccadilly, in Manchester, which is about eight or nine miles away, and 155ft above the service reservoir at Denton. The flow of water is entirely by gravity.

Engine beds ready for delivery, Bottoms Quarry. The skills portrayed by the stonemasons at Bottoms Quarry were not only utilised for the work of the great reservoirs (see p.80, recording the valve foundations). The stone engine beds shown above were used as foundations to fasten down steam-engines pumping water from the bore holes in Manchester.

Godley Reservoir under construction. Work commenced in July 1850 and was completed a year later. The photograph highlights the portion of the reservoir showing the cluster of valves which are used to control the inlet and outlet flows of water to and from the reservoir.

two

1848 – Construction Work Commences

The turnpike road to Saltersbrook and Sheffield (A628) passed along one side of the valley, and the Manchester, Sheffield and Lincolnshire Railway (made redundant in 1982) passed down the other side, and where these approached one another was to be the location of the dam. The height of the dam was 90ft above the level of the river, 30ft wide at the top, with a slope of 3:1 on the reservoir side, and 2:1 on the down-stream side. The inner slope was to be pitched with stone 18in thick.

A portion of the turnpike road was submerged by the new reservoir and had to be accordingly diverted and carried over the top of the new dam. Two main streams entered the reservoir: at its upper end, the river Etherow, which also received drainage water from the Woodhead Railway Tunnel, and the Heyden Brook, which flowed into the proposed reservoir via a tributary on the north side of the valley.

Overflow weirs were constructed across these two streams, which would form Residuum Lodges, used to settle out the turbid or discoloured water in times of flooding before it entered the reservoir.

Sand and silt deposited in the lodges could then be removed as and when necessary, thus maximising the storage capacity of the reservoir. Upstream to each of the Residuum Lodges, the water was to be conveyed in masonry channels, constructed especially to by-pass the flood water during the building of the reservoir dam.

The overflow waste weir on the first Woodhead Embankment, 1851. If you fill an empty mug with tea and keep on pouring, the tea overflows. A reservoir acts in a similar fashion – once filled with water, it overflows. The photograph shows the Woodhead Reservoir overflow, often referred to as the Overflow Waster Weir.

The original position of the discharge pipes through the first Woodhead Embankment. Note the steam crane on the left of the picture, and also the travelling winch and gantry. The stone portal and the door to the valve house is also visible. The continuation of the central core below original ground level is referred to as the 'cut-off trench', meaning it cuts off the leakage beneath the dam. Depending on its depth, the cut-off trench was often filled with concrete rather than clay, to withstand the greater pressure of water. It was abandoned on construction of the second Woodhead Embankment.

The earthen dam of the reservoir was to be sealed by forming a clay puddle core-wall the full length of the dam. This consisted of an impermeable 'clay puddle' central core or curtain, which was supported on either side by selected strong earth material. It is the puddle core which seals off the dam or embankment from leakage (see photographs on page 32 and drawings on pages 67 and 75).

An interesting feature was the construction of a masonry bridge consisting of nine arches of 9.14m (30ft) each span. This viaduct linked the Saltersbrook Turnpike Road across the northerly side of the reservoir, through which Heyden Brook flowed.

Little did Bateman know that the construction of the Woodhead Dam was to be epic, for the Woodhead Reservoir was the first reservoir to be commenced and the last to be concluded, in 1877; it was thirty long and tedious years before a perfect and watertight dam could be completed.

Bateman's first project for the supply of water to Manchester from the Pennine chain of hills was actually designed in 1844. He must have been satisfied when, at last, in August 1848, Woodhead Reservoir was contracted out to Messrs Richard Thompson & Sons of Blackburn. It was the first reservoir where work began.

Woodhead Reservoir, looking south-westerly towards the Heyden Viaduct, from the Heyden Brook end of the reservoir. The viaduct, which was completed in 1851, consists of nine masonry arches and is commonly called Nine Holes. The traffic was turned over the new Manchester to Saltersbrook turnpike road in the same year.

29 November 1848

Woodhead Reservoir,

I am in communication with the Sheffield Railway Company to ascertain the cost of putting a siding at the Woodhead Reservoir for the delivery of the pipes close to the spot at which they will be required. I find the cost of carting from the Woodhead Station to the embankment will be at least £40, probably more.

I believe I omitted to state that I had appointed Egerton Halifax Williams as the Puddle Tinter at Woodhead when those works were commenced. He has been constantly engaged of the last 5 or 6 years in a similar capacity and is an honest and valuable servant. I have been paying him 24/- per week both that amount and his appointment will require your confirmation.

Bateman had been informed that the Liverpool Corporation had recently bought iron-pipes which could be seen at Birkenhead, 'all corroded by rust from long exposure to the elements'.

Knowing only too well that his own cast-iron pipes would be exposed to the winters of the Longdendale Valley before they would be required for use, he decided to find a means of preserving them from the same fate.

19 December 1848

Dr Angus Smith,

I have to bring before your notice a process of preventing the corrosion of Iron Pipes which I now feel myself in a condition to recommend for your adaption.

It is an application of coal-pitch or asphaltum for which Dr R.A. Smith has recently taken out a patent.

An effective, and at the same time economical mode of preventing the oxidation of water pipes has been for many years a, subject of anxious consideration and enquiry. The most generally adapted, and I believe hitherto the most effective process, has been that of coating the inside of the pipes with a wash of hydraulic lime. This however is generally very inefficient and unsatisfactory and almost useless in the case of very soft water. The extreme of softness of the Longdendale waters and the testimony of Dr Dalton of Hollingworth, an accomplished chemist is that it was particularly destructive of iron, rendered the question with reference to the supply of Manchester one of unusual anxiety and importance.

Bateman later explained that in order to drive off any rust or dampness, and to allow the coal-pitch to penetrate the pores of the iron – which to some extent were opened by the heating – the pipes were first heated in a vertical pan, and then immersed in another containing the boiling liquid. They were sufficiently coated by being slowly let down by a travelling crane on a 'gantry', before being drawn up again. The pipes had previously been subjected to hydraulic pressure in a proving press equal to a column of water 300ft in height.

Bateman must be given much of the credit for establishing a process which later became universally accepted, and for which the Longdendale pipes have since proved.

4 January 1849

I am sorry to report that the works at the Mottram Tunnel continue to be carried on in such an unsatisfactory manner that I feel it is my duty to certify that Mr Graham is not proceeding with the work at the rate that is likely to complete it at the time agreed upon nor is he performing the several operations in a workmanlike manner. I must therefore recommend that you give him immediately the requisite notice and take the work out of his hands.

The Shires hauling 40in-diameter cast-iron pipes at Vale House Reservoir, 1898

Woodhead:

Left: *Puddle-trench construction, Cheshire (North) side, Woodhead Reservoir, 1872 (second embankment). Further to the explanation regarding puddle cores on page 29, this photograph shows the puddle trench being constructed below the original ground level. This trench (No.3) was excavated to a depth of 105ft; the sides were supported by string timber, referred to as shuttering. The trench was then filled with wet puddled clay in layers of 6in. Wearing clogs or strong boots with sacking tied around their ankles and lower legs, the men trod the clay with their feet, adding fresh layers of clay until the final height of the dam had been completed. In the background of the picture there is a steam crane lifting out the excavated rock. Note the wooden chute in the foreground, which was used for carrying the water from the river Etherow across and away from the working area.*

Below left: *A close-up view of No.1 puddle trench, Woodhead Reservoir.*

Below right: *This sketch shows a triple-slide 48in-diameter valve, typical of the triple slides installed at Longdendale. The gate of the valve was constructed in three separate pieces: a left-hand slide, a middle slide and a right-hand slide. This, together with the gearing, contributed to make the opening of the valve much easier to operate under the great pressure of water exerted against the gate of the valve.*

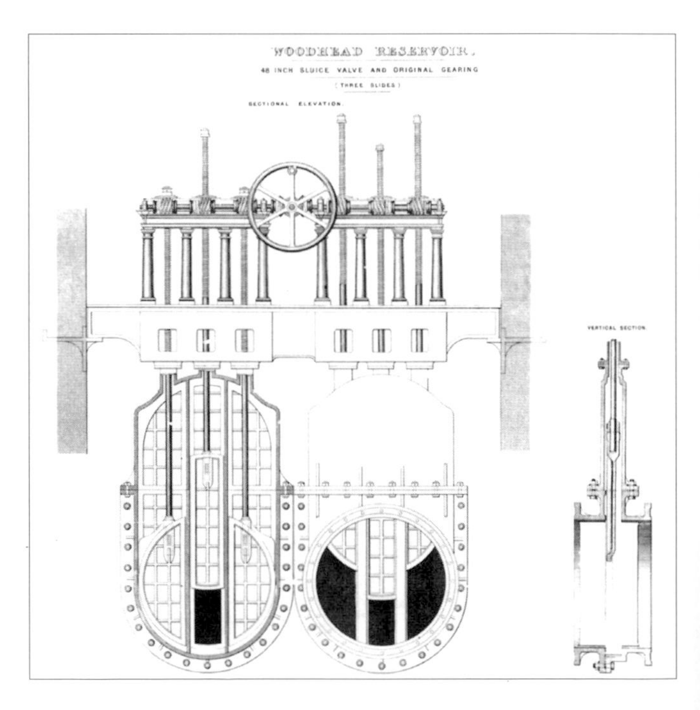

17 January 1849

Mottram Tunnel,

In pursuance of your resolution of the 11th inst. I attended at Mottram on Saturday last the 13th inst. and took possession of the works and materials upon Mr Graham's Contract.

I directed an Inventory to be made of all the machinery, materials and implements upon the ground, and each article to be branded or otherwise marked with Mr Graham's marks or initials.

Mr Graham did not attend himself but I obtained from Mr Barnett, his assistant, all the information he could afford with relation to arrangements for land, stone and the contracts which had been entered into for carrying on the works.

I examined all the unpaid accounts contained in the Schedule furnished by Mr Graham. I found that they were substantially all correct but that the list contained only a portion of those which are actually unpaid. Including unpaid wages and disputed accounts it appears that there are further demands upon Mr Graham to the extent of about £250.

J.F. Bateman, the man of strict business principles, shows himself to be a warm hearted generous man as Fred Bateman pays out starving workmen and their families from his own pocket.

The wages of the men were due upon a fortnight's pay on Saturday, but there was no provision for paying them. The workpeople employed by a sub-contractor by the name of Wallwork, to which Mr Graham had gradually let nearly the whole of the work, had not been paid for many weeks. The men were in a state of starvation and I therefore advanced them what money I had about me to help them on until they could either obtain their wages or other work.

I paid £21-7-0 principally to the men working for Mr Graham. It would be very desirable that an arrangement should be if possible be made with Mr Graham for the discharge of all his debts and I therefore suggested to Mr Barnett the proposal of some person attending the next common meeting duly authorised on the part of Mr Graham to enter into such an arrangement.

I then received tenders for the execution of the works and have let the whole to respectable men in four different lots.

Operations were commenced on Monday morning at both ends and at five out of seven shafts, arrangements are making for going on at the remaining two and materials of all descriptions have been ordered, and as far as time has permitted, for carrying on the work with vigour.

With reference to management I have appointed as Bookkeeper and Timekeeper at a salary of 30/- per week, Mr Edwin Smith, who has filled a similar situation for seven years in Lord Ellesmere's employ at Worsley.

As superintendent of the Stonework, Mr Robert Taylor of Mossley, an experienced Stone Mason and Builder, at a salary of £80 per year, with a promise of an increase. He has not been employed in a similar capacity before, but I have every reason to believe him an honest and competent man.

Much of the increased labour and responsibility of the work will involve upon my Mining Inspector, Mr Molyneux, and I have therefore suggested that you give him £50 a year more than the sum I allow him.

Wharf at Hyde. I have for some time been in negotiation with Mr Bradbury of the Clayton Colliery for the use of a very convenient wharf upon the Peak Forest Canal at Hyde, now in the possession of himself and his partners. I last week received a communication from him, that they would grant entire use of the wharf, which is possibly about 2,500 yards in extent, and the use of the weighing machine upon the ground, for a rent of £2 per week for as long or short a time as we may choose to occupy it. It is a very convenient situation for the delivery of the 40 inch pipes, and the wharf will allow ample space for the erection of the pipe proving machines and the coating apparatus.

Bateman's control of his labour force, especially his stonemasons, can better be understood from an account he describes in his *History and Description of the Manchester Waterworks.*

> The tunnel was lined for the greater part with stone 9in in thickness set in Ardwick lime mortar – a lime which, although slow in setting, eventually sets hard under water. When the work was partly finished there was a threatened turn out of the masons. There was clay in the immediate neighbourhood above the tunnel, and on hearing of what was going to happen, I immediately made contracts for making it into bricks, and before the men knew what I was about, I had about two millions of bricks stacked ready to be used in case of a 'turn-out'. The appearance of the bricks, however, was sufficient to keep the masons at work, and the bricks were all used in lining the tunnel before it was completed.

The section of brickwork referred to can be seen on inspection of Mottram Tunnel.

The overflow weir of the Woodhead Reservoir Lodge (Etherow Pool). The lodge would be emptied of water by opening the scour valve, the opening being in the centre at the bottom of the masonry, as shown on the photograph. On the left is the Millowners Watercourse, used to carry water to supply the mills lower down the valley. (See a further description of a residuum lodge on page 28).

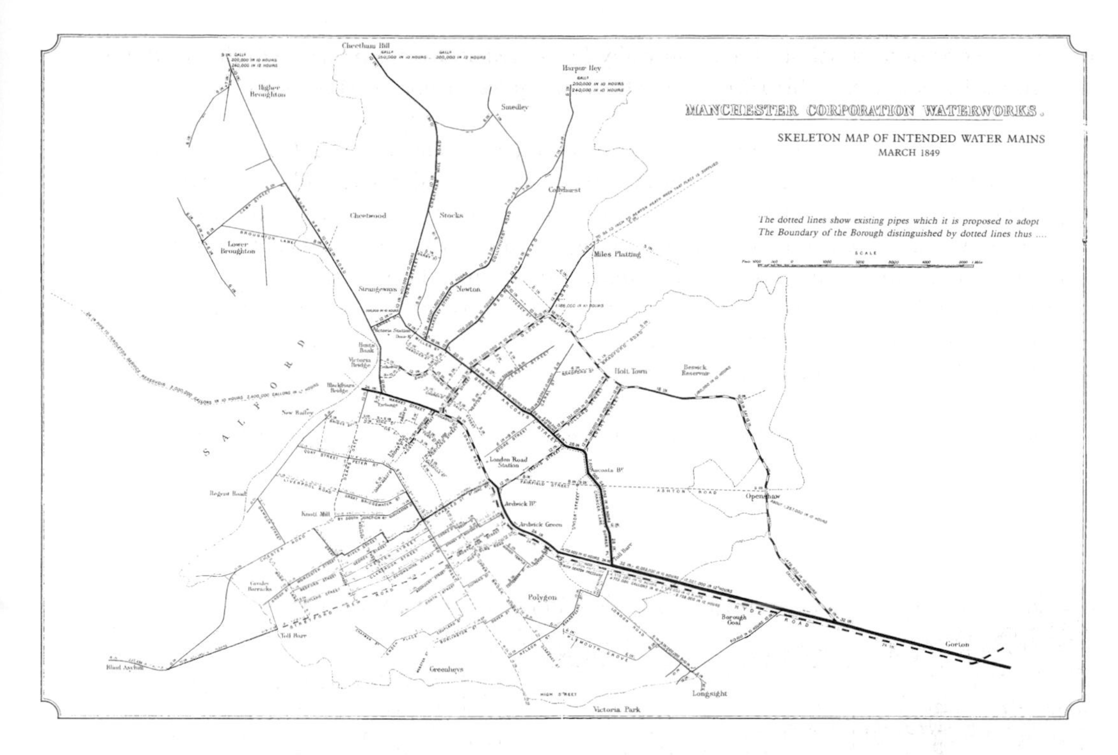

Skeleton map of intended water mains, Manchester Corporation Waterworks, March 1849.

5 May 1849

A cottage and outbuilding, the residence of one of the Duke of Norfolk's gamekeepers will be covered by water. The Duke's agent, Mr Tomlinson has applied to me about it as they are anxious to make arrangements for building another. The value they put on the whole is £200.

Crowden Schoolhouse,

Messrs Thompson have estimated the cost of building a school room – 12 yards by 8 yards, furnished with seats for the accommodation of 100 persons and with desks for scholars and schoolmaster at £130.

The Rhodeswood Reservoir and partial construction of Torside Reservoir was let to Mr Merritt, in April 1849, and managed by his agent, Mr Golden.

The Arnfield and Hollingworth Contract was commenced during the month of May 1849, and it is interesting to note that the embankments of these two reservoirs had to be composed entirely of clay, as no other material was to be found in the immediate neighbourhood. The overflow water from these reservoirs was discharged into a smaller reservoir below, called Waste Lodge, which was originally constructed for the supply of a mill on the Hollingworth stream. On completion of these works, the drinking water was carried from the reservoirs by cast-iron pipes leading into the same watercourse which carried the waters from the Longdendale Valley to the Mottram Tunnel, and subsequently to the Godley Reservoir.

Bateman informs us:

> On excavating for the formation of these embankments, various shells, both univalves and bivalves, apparently similar to existing species on the Lancashire shore, were met with, although the elevation of the ground in which they were discovered was 550 feet above the level of the sea, and at least 40 miles distant. From this it may be inferred that the clay of the district was at one time beneath or on the level of the sea, and that it has been (geologically speaking) only recently elevated.

The year 1849 was no exception for 'hands in the till', with its obvious subsequent results.

> Mr Jardine the clerk at the Wharf, I discharged last week in consequence of drunkedness and fraudulous wage bills. A very careful analysis of his accounts I lay before you, from which it, appears that a few shillings are still due to him. His place must be filled up by another appointment.

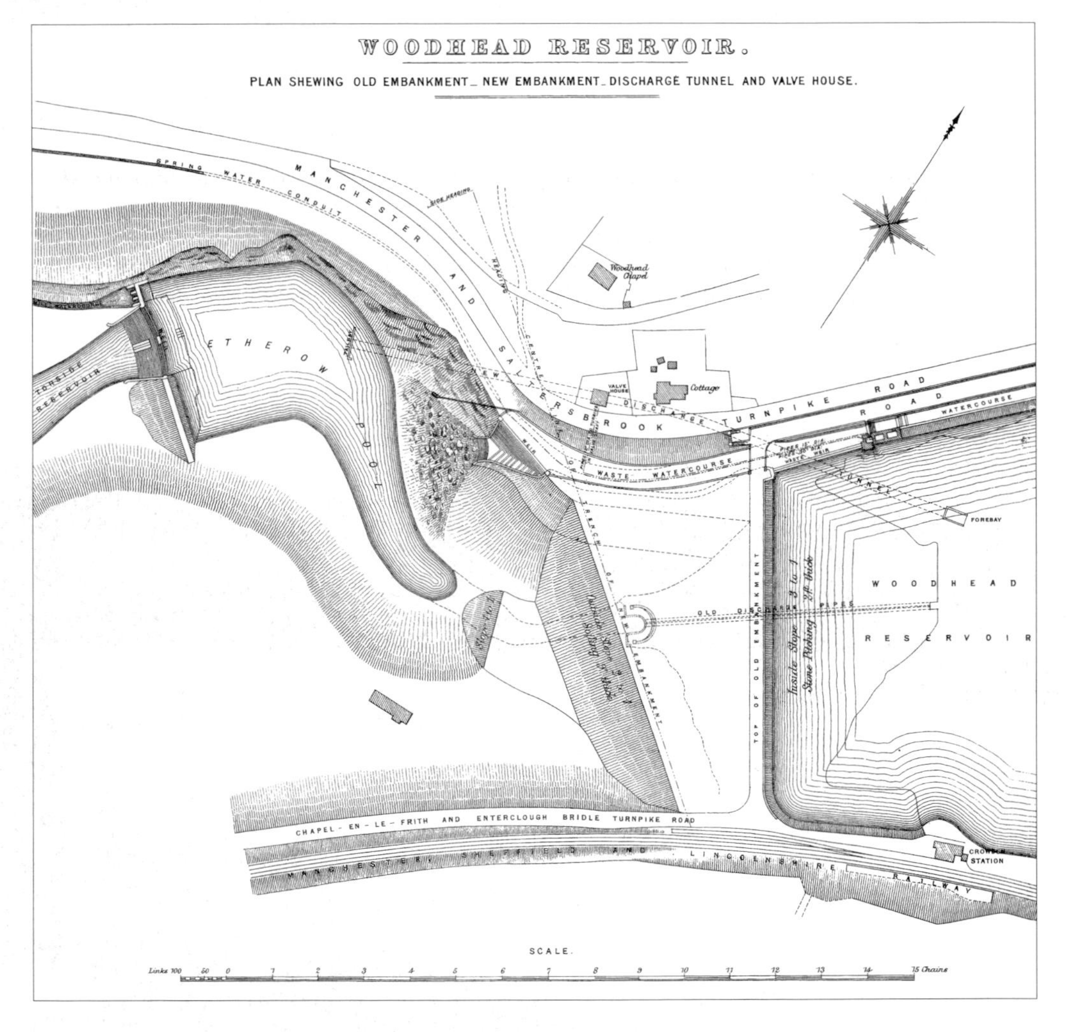

Plan showing the old embankment, new embankment, discharge tunnel and valve house, Woodhead Reservoir.

The settling ponds, as their name implies, were designed and constructed to give the raw, discoloured water time for the suspended and colloidal matter to gravitate to the bottom of the pond (similar to the residuum lodges). The ponds were abandoned on the advent of the more sophisticated treatment plants. The water was fed into the ponds from pipes at ground level; the clearest water contained in the top layers was fed back into the aqueduct through pipes positioned at the top water level of the pond.

It is lunchtime on the settling ponds at Arnfield Reservoir.

8 October 1849

Torside Reservoir,

The Embankment of the Torside Reservoir is to be raised to its full height at the scheduled prices of Mr Merritt's present contract. The Torside Embankment, to be completed by the time the Rhodeswood should have been, and a longer time allowed for the latter.

The necessity of pushing forward this work is I am sorry to say rendered more important than ever in consequence of serious injury done to the Woodhead Reservoir by a very heavy flood which occurred on Sunday.

A consequence of the 1848 Act was that the mill owners had pressed for the construction of the Rhodeswood Reservoir without further delay, in order that they would benefit from their extra supply of compensation water, via the proposed mill owners' gauging weir.

If the Rhodeswood Reservoir, which was the third of the chain, had been completed and allowed to fill, then the foundations for the Torside Reservoir embankment could have drowned with water. In order to avoid this, it was necessary for Bateman to construct the base of Torside Reservoir embankment in dry conditions to a height of some 20ft. This would then mean that the Torside embankment would have been, although only partly completed, a little higher than the Rhodeswood Reservoir top water level.

This involved, therefore, constructing the lower part of the Torside puddle wall and laying the two lines of 48in-diameter discharge pipes, to be controlled by 36in-diameter valves at the outer end of the embankment. These discharge arrangements were eventually to be abandoned.

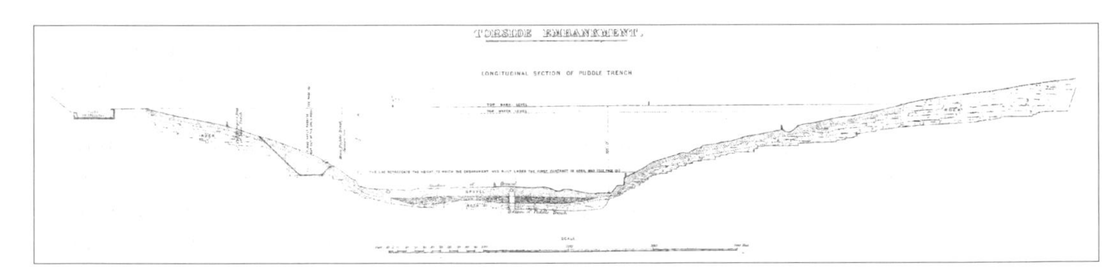

Sketch showing the height that the Torside embankment required to avoid drowning.

If Bateman ever suffered from nightmares, they would have undoubtedly contained an horrific flood of catastrophic proportions, with equally horrendous results. In July 1848, a gigantic flood had occurred in the vicinity of Blackburn which caused extensive damage at Darwen, and resulted in the collapsing of an embankment of a private reservoir, terminating in the tragic drowning of twelve people. Bateman had immediately familiarised himself with the volume and conditions of the flood and, using this knowledge, he wisely redesigned his flood conditions for the Longdendale Valley. It was ironic that twelve months after he wrote that very report, the Great Flood of Sunday 7 October 1849 occurred. Bateman described it in vivid and realistic terms to his Waterworks Committee.

12 October 1849

Gentlemen, I am sorry to have to report serious injury which occurred at the Woodhead reservoir on Sunday last. The weir erected across Heyden brook for the purpose of diverting the flood waters, during the execution of the reservoir embankment, along the new watercourse constructed for the same purpose, gave way under the overwhelming force of an extraordinarily heavy flood accompanied by a violent gale of wind, which materially increased the pressure upon the stonework.

Torside embankment, looking west towards Rhodeswood (originally spelled Rhodes Wood). North and south valve houses are now demolished. Rhodeswopod Reservoir was completed in 1855.

This weir gave way, as nearly as can be ascertained, about two o'clock pm, after which it, the water no longer able to pass along the new watercourse, impounded in the basin of the reservoir till, at half-past five, it reached the top of the embankment, which had been raised to about 24 feet about the mouth of the discharge pipes, and further raised three feet during the progress of the flood by the utmost exertions of the contractor's men. After reaching this point, the water flowed over the top, speedily cutting a breach for the escape of the whole body of impounded water, amounting at that time to 17 or 18,000,000 cubic feet.

The water thus let loose, rushed down the valley, destroying fences, crops, bridges, and buildings in its course for about five miles below the reservoir. The damage to the land is not considerable – the more serious injury is to works and buildings.

Mr Merritt, the contractor for the Rhodeswood and Torside embankment has had a considerable quantity of ashlar stone carried away, besides planks, barrows, waggons and tools. His works been otherwise injured and impeded.

At Vale House mills the injury has been extensive – the goit leading the water to the mill has been partly washed away and filled up. A schoolhouse, the end of a small building, and a good many high fence walls have been washed down. The water got into the cellar of the mill and has damaged a larger number of calico pieces. Other damage has been done to the premises but the machinery has principally escaped. The cottages adjoining the mill have suffered considerably as well as the gardens belonging to the cottagers. A bridge over the river has been partly washed down.

At Rhodes' mill, the next below, a timber bridge across the river has been carried away, the water- wheel injured, and some power-looms submerged, besides other damage of no very serious amount.

At Bottoms mill, the banks of the goit have been damaged and some of the premises partly filled with water, besides injury to roads, fences &c.

Flood damage at Wilmer Clough, above the railway, August 1900.

At Waterside the water got into some cottages and washed down some walls and pigsties, and did other damage of no serious amount.

At Messrs Dalton's print-works a wooden bridge across the river has been washed away, and the works damaged, to some extent by the water getting into the premises.

Beyond this point I have heard of no damage of consequence.

Had the rain ceased at three or four o'clock or had the embankment been 40 feet in height, it is almost certain that no injury would have been sustained.

The weir was evidently broken down by the continued and violent beating of the waves created by the hurricane which swept straight down the Heyden valley, and which finally shook the ashlar top of the weir so as to allow the water to escape.

I have also engaged Mr Dearnally to ascertain the damage to crops and dwelling houses and employed Messrs Harrop and Dearnally of Tintwistle to estimate the injury sustained to the buildings at the Vale House Mill.

Flood damage creating a gap in the wall of Turnpike Road near the quarry, Torside, August 1900.

14 November 1849

Public House,

I have met Mr Cawley, Mr Tollemache's agent a few days ago with reference to the alterations or the rebuilding of the Angel Inn.

It appears that the alterations of the house will cost nearly as much as the building of a reservoir, including the expense we shall have to incur lowering the ground floor to meet the views and wishes of Mr Tollemache.

I would therefore reconsider the arrangement being made for a new house.

10 January 1850

At the Mottram Tunnel I am sorry to have to report a serious accident to Mr Molyneux, the Mining Inspector and Robert Taylor, the Inspector of Masonry which occurred on Friday last and for the particulars of which I will refer you to Mr Mawson's report:

'At one of the shafts (No.5) 205 feet in depth, a serious accident befell my two inspectors, Molyneux and Taylor. They were going down together in a tub, when the engine-driver started at so great a speed that Molyneux called to him not to go so fast, when he checked his engine too suddenly and stripped the teeth of the cogwheel attached to the drum round which the rope was wound. Thus set at liberty beyond all control, the tub, with the two men in it, descended the shaft as rapidly as it could unwind the rope from the drum. There was a sump-well at the bottom covered by 3 inch planks, and such was the impetus of the fall that the tub went through these planks. One man (Molyneux) has a compound fracture of one leg, and the other man had his ribs broken.'

In his *History and Description of the Manchester Waterworks*, Bateman tells us that both men recovered and remained in his service for several years, and added, 'It was a wonder they were not both killed, but luckily for them the rope and head stocks did not follow; had they done so they could not have escaped destruction'.

Flood damage at a bridge under the railway, Torside Brook, August 1900.

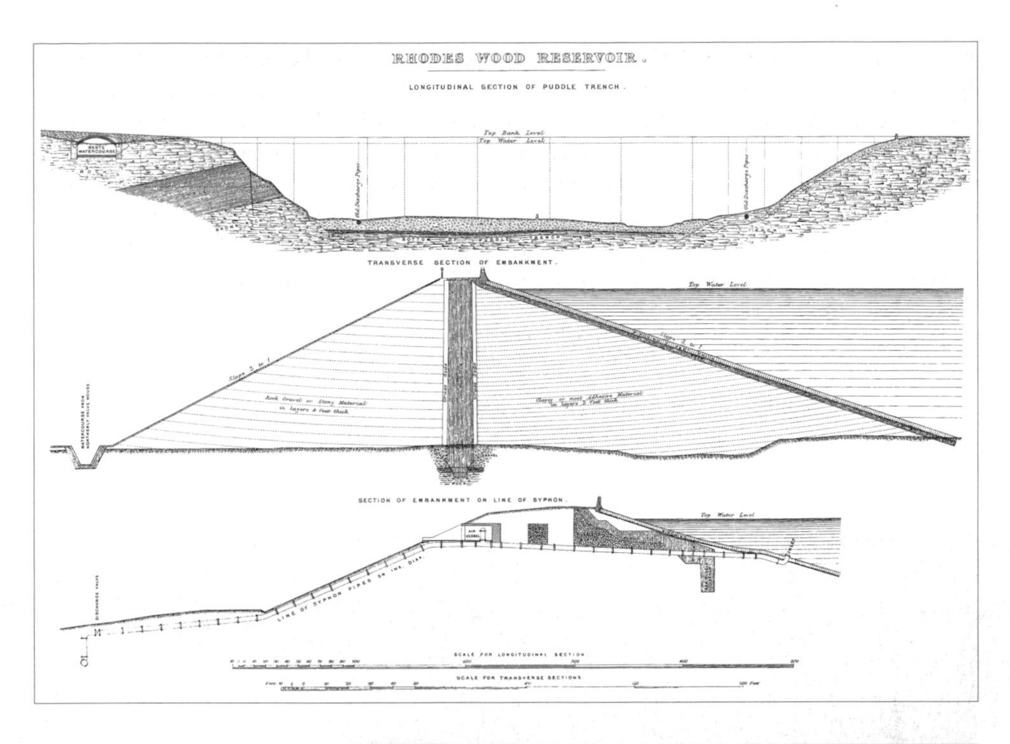

Above: *A drawing of Rhodeswood Reservoir.*

Right: *Flood damage at Anfield watercourse.*

Settling tanks at River Etherow, Woodhead, originally used to take drainage from Woodhead railway tunnel (1890).

16 January 1850

Nearly all of the works except the driving of the Mottram Tunnel and the laying of the pipes at Denton Reservoirs and in the Hyde Road are stopped in consequence of the continuance of this severe frost. Several hundred men are now idle though operations at the Hyde Wharf being also at a standstill for want of pipes, no boats being able to reach Hyde from Wigan for weeks.

18 April 1850

The names of the parties having the management and inspection of the various contracts are:

At Woodhead:

Resident Engineer	Mr Alfred Moore – Glossop (who also has the laying out and control of the watercourses still to be let)
Inspector	Mr David Bain – Woodhead
Puddle Tinter	Egerton Halifax Williams – Woodhead

At Torside & Rhodes Wood:

Resident Engineer	Mr George H. Hill – Tintwistle
Inspector	Mr Macquire
Puddle Tinters	At Torside – Thomas Handyside Cole At Rhodes Wood – Cole (Junior)

At Hollingworth & Arnfield:

Resident Engineer	Mr George H. Hill
Puddle Tinters	At Arnfield Bank – Robert Cooper At Hollingworth – William Travis

At Hollingworth Watercourse –
Mottram Tunnel & Tetley Fold Watercourse:

Resident Engineer	Mr John J. Mawson
Mining Inspector	Mr John Molyneux
Masonry Inspector	Mr Robert Taylor

At Godley Reservoir:

Engineer In Charge	Mr James Hayes
Inspector	Ralph Doukin (Senior)
Puddle Tinter	Joseph Cooper
Pipe Laying Inspector	Ralph Doukin (Junior)

At Denton Reservoir:

Engineer In Charge	Mr T.B. Foster
Inspector	Ralph Doukin (Junior)
Puddle Tinter	Joseph Brightly

A puddle tinter was an important man. It was he who controlled the quality of the puddle and had to decide whether the consistency was correct when puddling the raw clay with water. The puddle core wall was built within the dam, and was compacted by men treading the puddle with their feet.

Laying the 40in-diameter cast-iron main from Rhodeswood to Arnfield (near Tintwhistle recreation ground), whence Conduit Street, Tintwhistle, derived its name. Note the complete absence of mechanical appliances.

30th May 1850

I lay before you drawings of a proposed Wind Mill for raising water at Mottram for the supply of parties from whence water has been abstracted and Mr Mawson's Estimate of that need and other various modes of obtaining such supply. The probable cost of the Wind Mill and pumps appear to be about £650.

I attended yesterday, in pursuance of instructions received from the Town Clerk, at Rhodeswood for the purpose of taking possession of the land purchased from Mr Hyde. There were Watchers upon the ground and I went over and informed Mr Hyde's son, but no opposition was offered to our security upon the ground. The land was staked and fenced off and the excavation for the Waste Weir was at once commenced.

Water to Manchester and Salford

It is interesting to note that in 1835, the landowners in the Longdendale Valley were paid large sums of money for their land by the Sheffield, Ashton-Under-Lyne & Manchester Railway Co. in the race to build railways. The landowners again expected exorbitant prices to be paid by Manchester Corporation for the required land. George Hyde, of Tintwistle, demanded £7,000 for his land at Rhodeswood; the Corporation offered him £1,100; a tribunal awarded him £1,600. Mr Hyde decided to fight his case in court. The litigation which followed resulted in him becoming a ruined man.

For Bateman, the year 1850 ended with the gratifying fact that the people of Manchester and Salford would be drinking pure water from the Longdendale Valley.

Original overflow weir at Torside Reservoir, seen from the north end of the bridge.

He had reported to his Committee that the water had been sent through the Mottram Tunnel for the first time on 17 October, but it is from elsewhere we learn that two days later, Bateman inspected the Mottram Tunnel in a flat-bottomed boat. He was accompanied by his Assistant Engineer, Mr George H. Hill; his Tunnel Resident Engineer, Mr John J.Mawson; his Mining Inspector, Mr John Molyneux; and the Contractor for the Hollingworth and Arnfield Reservoirs, Mr Samuel Taylor. Five men in a boat on a journey which was safely accomplished in one hour and forty minutes, a journey that Bateman would have ever remembered with pride and a satisfied sense of achievement, a journey which perhaps fortified him in his difficult task ahead.

23 January 1851

Burst Iron Pipe

The delivery of the water to the Gorton Reservoir has been interrupted by the burst of pipe in the town ef Hyde, on Tuesday the 14th inst. after my last report had been written. The pipes and valves had been tested with the full pressure of the water above Broomstairs Bridge on the Monday and again on the Tuesday without any incident, although here and there a leaky joint was discovered. On the Tuesday evening, and shortly after I had left the ground, after a minute examination of the whole line of pipes, a burst took place in the centre of the town of Hyde, when the pressure was about 130 feet, and a few hundred yards below the self-acting valve near the 'Lockups'. A piece about six feet in length was blown out of the side of the pipe and a tremendous rush of water instantly ensued. The increased velocity acted back upon the self-acting valve which almost immediately closed and in a few minutes the rush of water ceased.

Some damage was done, the claim for which amounted to between £40 and £50 but which may be arranged for a little more than £30.

The accident is valuable as proving the entire efficiency of the self-acting valves and the important advantage which has been gained by their introduction. The accident occurred in such a situation that the damage would have been immense without such a precaution. The breach has been repaired by the putting down of another pipe and the street restored. The Upper Gorton Reservoir is still full and running over.

19 February 1851

Woodhead Reservoir,

The embankment at Woodhead Reservoir is 20 feet of the full height which, when the work is completed, will be 90 feet above the old bed of the river. There only remains about 28,000 cubic yards of earthworks to execute.

The Heyden Viaduct and the diversion of the Manchester and Saltersbrook Turnpike Road are finished and the traffic is turned over the new road.

The large valves for discharging the water have been delivered and fixed to the pipes. They have been beautifully executed by Messrs Armstrong & Co. of Newcastle-upon-Tyne.

The number of men employed upon all the works out of the borough is about 1,100.

Mr Armstrong was the founder of Messrs Armstrong and Co., who supplied all the original valves at Woodhead, Torside and Rhodeswood Reservoirs, including the principal valves on the City Piping. Previous to designing the hydraulic valves, Armstrong had invented the Hydraulic Crane, in 1847, and was later knighted Sir W.G. Armstrong. He founded the firm of Armstrong Whitworth, in which he perfected the first breech-loading gun. Queen Victoria elevated him to a baron in 1887.

Above: *Torside embankment, showing the flood watercourse on the left (the valve houses are now demolished).*

Below: *By comparison with modern methods, major works of the period were undertaken with the help of only limited powered plant, such as this steam crane and – in the background – a steam traction engine.*

11 March 1851

Labour Requirements,

In compliance with your request contained in your resolution of 5th inst. I have considered the arrangements which it will be necessary to make for the proper inspection and superintendence of the Work outside the Borough when finished. The following is a list of the places, at which men will have to reside, their duties, and probably wages:

1 Man at Woodhead to attend to the Reservoirs and the weirs and watercourses near; wages from 20*s* to 24*s* per week

1 Man at Torside, similar duties 20*s* to 24*s* per week

1 Man at Rhodeswood to attend to the Reservoir and the Rhodeswood Conduit gauging the water for the Mills – Supplying Water to Manchester etc. 24*s* per week

1 Man at Arnfield to attend to the Afnfield and Hollingworth Reservoirs and to the Watercourses near – Supplying Water to manchester. 24*s* per week

1 Man at the Godley End of the Mottram Tunnel, will be partially employed in watching and protecting the Works, and in assisting at the Godley Reservoir, – say – 18*s* per week

1 Man at Godley Reservoir in attending to the Reservoir straining and supplying water to Manchester and in taking charge of the main pipe through Hyde at Broomstair Bridge 24*s* per week

At each of the above places, a Cottage must be erected and Men appointed should be superior, trustworthy Men, with some amount of Education. Those at the Upper Reservoirs, ready hands at spade-work, walling or masonry – those at Godley and Denton, tolerable mechanics or at all events good pipe-layers.

It will be necessary to employ four or five labourers to attend to the Watercourses on the Moors etc., the Residuum Lodge and to assist in keeping all clean and in good repair at about 18/- per week – say in all twelve regularly employed Men.

The Outdoor Superintendent begs to report to the Water Works Committee as follows: That it appears desirable that lanterns should be provided for the men who gauge the water flowing over the Weirs at Woodhead Reservoir and the Hollingworth Water Course.

Opposite above: *Valve house to Torside valve shaft. Another example of water engineering ingenuity of the mid-nineteenth century is this multi-valve control equipment which derived its motive power from a turbine operated by water in the aqueduct. Gearing enables any combination of the three main valves to be opened or closed by the movement on hand levers.*

Opposite, below left: *Longdendale Reservoir keeper, E.V. Davies, attending to moorland rain gauge in 1965. Eddie retired in 1967 after forty-two years' service with Manchester Corporation Works.*

Opposite, below right: *Excavating the 40in-diameter pipe trench at Rhodeswood.*

23 April 1851

Rhodeswood,

The works in all parts are making good progress. The only point of anxiety at present is the land-slip below Tintwistle Knarr. The ground is now moving rapidly forward – for some time back at the rate of ¾ of an inch a day where the foot has been cut away for the watercourse. It is not therefore prudent to pursue this cutting any further, and other means than those suggested when I last reported on the subject must be adapted, to arrest the further progress of the slip. This appears likely to be the best accomplished by so weighting the foot of the slip where it rests within the. site of the Rhodeswood Reservoir by a mass of rock and dry material, so as to counter balance the tendency to move. If the foot can in this way be secured from all movement, I do not think it will be very difficult to secure the ground at the level of the watercourse. Whatever is done requires to be done promptly and I have therefore given instructions to take such measures as appears to be at present the most likely to succeed.

And so work was commenced on the masonry-arch. The heavy retaining wall that Bateman had originally suggested was abandoned. In his *History and Description of the Manchester Waterworks*, Bateman tells us that the work was constructed under the superintendence of Mr Elias Smethurst, his masonry inspector. The foundations were laid on the upper side, in what appeared to be unmoved ground, and the lower side abutting against the material of the slip itself, which was prevented from further movement by a heavy mass of earth-rock placed against it and resting on the flat of the valley. The erection of the arch was quite successful, but some idea of the force it had to resist may be formed when it is stated that, although there was a space of 3ft in width at the back of the masonry, the slipping ground closed upon it twice during the operation of turning the first length of 15ft of the arch, and had to be cut off. During this operation, the ground moved downwards 9ft, and was finally arrested by the strength of the arch.

Rhodeswood Reservoir looking east in 1861. This was the area of the first landslip.

The masonry arch at Rhodeswood, which eventually resisted the landslip.

three

1852 – 1,000 Men at Work

A bridge over Torside Brook.

A field near Gamekeeper's cottage, Woodhead.

Flood Damage at Longdendale

10 February 1852

I am sorry that I shall be unable to attend your meeting tomorrow, owing to previous engagements of importance elsewhere, as I could have explained more fully than I have now more time for, the particulars of the heavy floods which we have experienced since Wednesday last 4th February.

The Manchester Guardian reported the full story:

The reservoirs of the Manchester Corporation Water works in the valley of Longdendale, which stood admirably the great floods of Wednesday and Thursday in last week, had a yet severer test in the continued heavy rains of the three following days, till on Sunday some of the reservoirs were within seven hours (supposing the rain had continued to fall in equal quantity during the whole of that time) of being brim-full; and there was consequently considerable anxiety on the subject, especially amongst the mill owners and other inhabitants of the valley within a little distance of and below the three great reservoirs of these works. This anxiety was of course greater than would otherwise have been the case, from the vivid remembrance of the recent horrors attending the bursting of the Bilbury Reservoir near Holmfirth, in Yorkshire; though there is analogy in the nature and character of the works to warrant any apprehension of the one because the other had failed, as for years past all conversant with it had expected it to do. In order to enable our more distant readers to comprehend the general character and vast extent of the Manchester Corporation Waterworks, and the circumstances which led to their position on Sunday last, we must enter a little into detail.

Old Paper Mill on Fair Vage Gutter, looking south. It was formerly Kidfield Mill, overlooking the south side of Torside Reservoir, Crowden.

Though in two instances, perhaps – one in Scotland and one in Ireland – there are single reservoirs larger than any of these of the Corporation Waterworks, yet, taken as a connected series or chain of artificial lakes, constructed for the storage water, those in the Longdendale Valley have the largest aggregate capacity of any artificial sheets of water in the world.

We learnt that on Wednesday and Thursday, the 4th and 5th instant. (February 1852), 'flood water to the extent of. 2.4in in the 24 hours was safely passed or impounded in the reservoirs, with a considerable space still remaining for storing additional water.

But before the stored water could be discharged from the reservoirs, a succession of other floods – especially during Saturday night and Sunday last – nearly exhausted the storage powers of the reservoirs; and on the evening of Sunday, the 8th, there remained provision only for the safe passage of heavy rain (which had then been continuing for some time) for a further period of six or seven hours.

With some amount of risk, though probably not very great, the continuance of rain for even 24 hours might have been provided for. Under these circumstances, however, the excitement of the mill owners and residents in the valley below the reservoirs, became very great during Sunday, stimulated, of course, by the recent catastrophe at Holmfirth; so that the whole valley was thronged by persons, many of whom came from some distance, notwithstanding the heavy continuous, and beating rains, to see the reservoirs, examine into their state, and speculate as to the possibility of some of their embankments giving way. A little inn, which, from its usual quietness and loneliness, has for its sign 'The Quiet Shepherd' was thronged from morning till night with people seeking shelter and refreshment; its stable and outbuildings were filled with guests, and the utmost excitement prevailed. On Sunday morning the rain continued to fall heavily from an early hour till about 2 o'clock p.m., without intermission. There was then a lull for nearly two hours, when it again commenced raining as heavily as ever, with a prospect of continuing during the night. Under these circumstances, Mr Bateman, who had been on the spot almost constantly from the morning of Thursday last, feeling the very great and solemn responsibility that would attach to him in case of any accident, even of a trifling nature, occurring to an embankment, without any notice to the inhabitants below, thought it prudent, about half-past three o'clock on Sunday afternoon, to despatch messengers to the parties immediately on the river, for some distance below the reservoirs – stating that, should it continue to rain heavily all night, some danger might be apprehended after the lapse of six or seven hours, and that it would therefore be prudent for them to prepare for the possibility of such a contingency. Of course this intimation spread great alarm throughout the valley, and the most vigorous efforts were made by some of the mill owners and others to remove valuable property without delay; the occupants of cottages and other dwellings along the stream also hastily removed their furniture to the houses of relatives and friends at some distance from the course of the stream.

Throughout the little village of Valehouse, the inhabitants were thrown into a state of the utmost consternation; for in the event of the bursting of the embankment, a large number of the houses must have been swept away. Some houses at Bottom's Mill would also have been in imminent danger, as would others occupied by operatives employed by Messrs Sidebottom at Waterside Mill; all these removed their furniture. Mr H. Lees, who resides between five and six miles below Torside, had carts and wagons constantly engaged for several hours in removing his household and other property. At Glossop the alarm was very general and much damage was done to furniture during its hasty removal.

Opposite above: *Old Paper Mill on Fair Vage Gutter, looking north.*

Opposite below: *Culvert under the turnpike road opposite Paper Mill on the south side of Torside Reservoir.*

Bottoms Lodge Mill, built before 1834 by John Winterbottom and used for cotton spinning and manufacturing, before it was owned by Manchester Corporation and leased to Robert Cross & Co. of Tintwhistle, in 1865.

> Fortunately, however, for all concerned, in the course of rather more than an hour after this intimation had been given by Mr Bateman, the weather cleared up; and as it promised well for the remainder of the night, and as the heavy flow of water during this interval had materially abated, he felt so confident of the perfect security of the works, that he dispatched other messengers, about half-past five p.m., to reassure the inhabitants, and to prevent or allay all unnecessary apprehension and alarm. The weather continued fine; the streams abated; and on Monday afternoon, the water within the reservoirs had been considerably diminished in quantity by the action of the discharge pipes.

Bateman later concluded the episode with poetic inspiration:

> The sun went down red and glowing with murky grandeur, dimly seen beneath the clouds, which, though breaking and clearing to the west, were then pouring down their contents in torrents at the place in which we stood. The rain gradually abated, and nearly ceased before six o'clock and I was satisfied that the worst was over, and all imminent danger was passed.

Bateman's report dated February 1852 draws his Committee's attention to a new and more complicated land-slip. It was lower down the flood watercourse than the previous one, and in the vicinity of Rhodeswood embankment. Earlier information not given in his reports, is referred to in his *History and Description of the Manchester Waterworks*, in which he states:

> On this ground, which exhibited no indication of moving, a contractor's village, called New Yarmouth, had been erected. This village was moved downwards about 8in during the night of the 6th of February; and the masonry of the waste weir and watercourse of the Rhodeswood Reservoir was crushed and disturbed. The completion of the embankment, which formed when finished, a buttress to the side of the valley, and the addition of weight to the toe of the moving mass, arrested the movement.

Up to that moment in time, Bateman had not only the confidence to deal with the first series and land-slips at the flood watercourse and turnpike road, but had successfully remedied the faults.

The waste weir at Rhodeswood, or overflow weir as it is commonly called, which was almost completed, had been badly damaged; a new blow had been dealt to hinder Bateman's progress. He now recognised that because the motion to this new slip was directed obliquely down the valley, he had a far more complicated problem to solve. The extent of ground moved was almost 30 acres, measuring about one third of a mile along the valley and 300-400ft in height. This mass had moved down the valley in the direction of the watercourse.

Bateman recommended to his Committee the two engineers he wished to consult regarding the land-slip. They were Mr Robert Stephenson, an eminent engineer who had achieved distinction for building railway bridges and son of the famous George Stephenson; and Mr Isambard Kingdom Brunel, Engineer to the Great Western Railway and eminent iron-ship designer. He also was the son of a celebrated father, Sir Marc Isambard Brunel.

The village of New Yarmouth set up on the northern side of Rhodeswood Reservoir, in which the construction workers and their families lived. It would appear from the picture that these 'shanty town' inhabitants were the lucky ones when compared with other workers, bearing in mind the atrocious conditions the Woodhead Tunnel employees and their families had to endure only ten years or so earlier.

Rhodeswood Reservoir, looking up the Longdendale Valley, 1861. The original overflow and flood watercourse are in the foreground.

31 March 1852

The best measures for adoption under these circumstances are now under consideration in connection with Mr Stevenson and Mr Brunel whose advice the Water Committee have allowed me to obtain.

On Saturday I accompanied Mr Stephenson and Mr Brunel over the works describing every part a directing their particular attention to the land-slips I am to meet them this week in London for the purpose of further consultation.

20 April 1852

Rhodes Wood Land Slip,

On Saturday last Mr Stephenson and Mr Brunel again examined this slip and considered the whole question most carefully. The practicability of tunnelling in the shale beneath the slip and of conveying the waste water away in recommendation of any plan until that point was ascertained. I have therefore to request your authority for sinking shafts and taking the necessary steps for ascertaining the depth of the moving ground and the character of the material beneath.

The dry weather has arrested the motion of the slip and no new feature is presented.

4 November 1852

Hollingworth and Arnfield Contracts,

Both Embankments are proceeding slowly and continuously. The Hollingworth bank is at present stationary but the other yields a little to the increased pressure.

20 January 1853

The leakage at Woodhead Reservoir remains the same – a little larger and a little discoloured.

I have carefully considered the question of how best to stop the leakage and I now beg to recommend that before anything else is done it should be attempted to be choked by sinking boreholes and pipes at the spot at which it is evident the escape is taking place and then pouring ashes and other choking material down the pipes under a considerable head of water

Arnfield Reservoir.

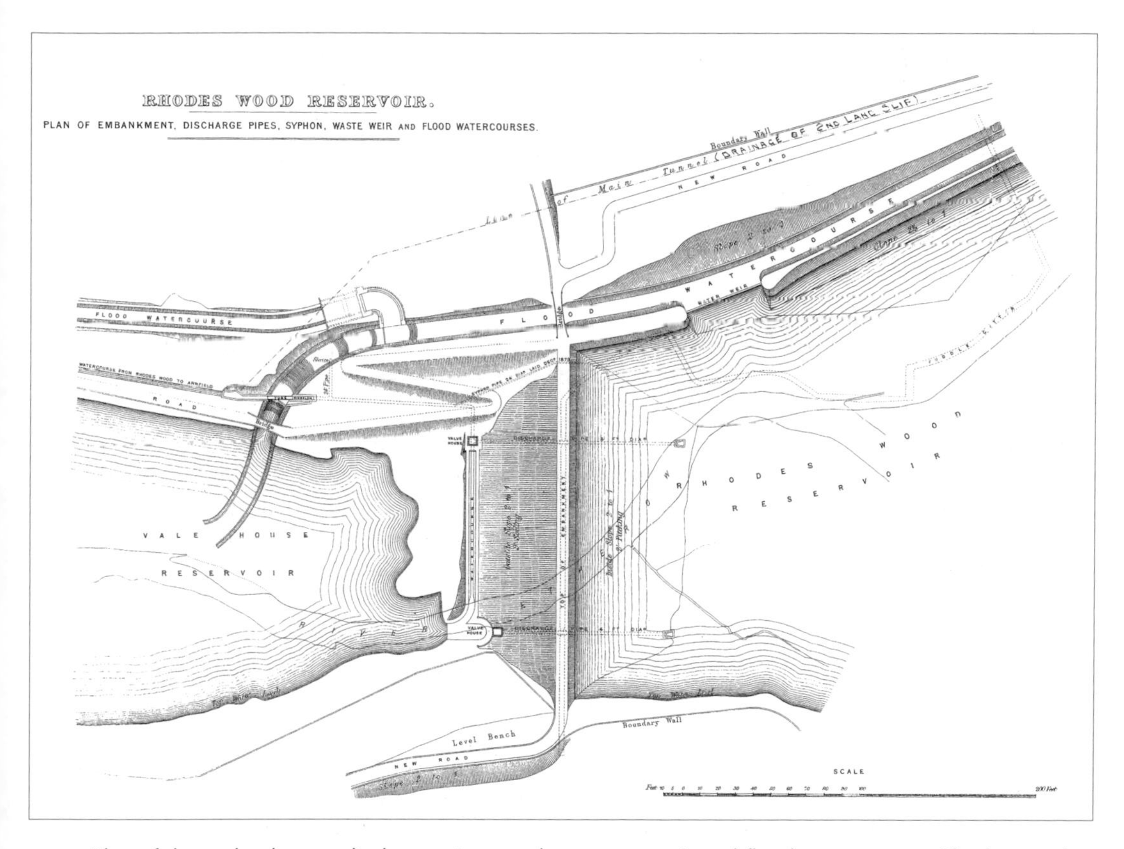

Plan of the embankment, discharge pipes, syphon, waste weir and flood watercourses, Rhodeswood Reservoir.

A few weeks and slight expense will prove if anything can be done by this means. If any good at all be done there will then be every possibility of curing it effectively. If not, another means must be devised.

27 April 1853

I hear that some delay is likely to arise in consequence of the workmen in the Valley having to come out for an increase in wages.

1 June 1853

Land Slip at Rhodes Wood,

The pipes, tunnels, and watercourse for the passage of pure water under the land-slip at Rhodes Wood, will I believe, be so far completed by the end of this week, that the supply of water through these works may be commenced and continued. Henceforth therefore, a full supply of pure water for the City may be ensured.

10 May 1854

Woodhead,

This completes the Woodhead Reservoir entirely with the exception of the operation of remedying the leakage'.

Bateman clearly reports the Woodhead Reservoir as being entirely completed – but was it?

That 'trifling leakage continued, and the boring and choking was persevered with, depending on the varying conditions of the reservoir at that time.

For the next eight years, Bateman's regular reports to his Committee constantly referred to the action of boring and choking, as he battled relentlessly to seal the leaking embankment of this troublesome reservoir.

Manchester Guardian Report

Dotted around the reservoirs on the hillsides, small shanty towns had sprung up to accommodate the navvies and their families. Houses, built of piled stones and mud, were thatched with ling from the moors, and many used potato sacks as doors:

A tragic incident concerning one family was reported in the *Manchester Guardian* on Saturday 26 August 1854:

> Sad death of two children. On Monday afternoon last, an inquest was held before Mr C. Hudson at the Black Bull, Tintwistle, on the remains of Joseph Forshaw, aged two years, and Robert Forshaw, aged four years, the children of James and Ann Forshaw, who resided in a hut near the first milestone from Tintwistle, on the Woodhead Road, no other habitations being nearer than 400 yards. The hut in question was only one storey high, and was built of rough stones and clay, and covered with straw thatch. It had two rooms, in one of which there were beds for six lodgers, and in the other there was sleeping accommodation for the father, mother and three children. The mother's statement was to the effect, that she generally arose at 4 a.m. in the morning, in order that her husband, who was a sub-contractor under Mr Taylor, at the Arnfield Reservoir, and the lodgers, might go to their work in due time.

The tumbler sluices, designed by Bateman, were another concept in valve control. Instead of vertical slides to control the passage of water, a horizontal cast-iron cylinder, partially slotted along its entire length, pivots within the framework of the sluice. To close the valve, the solid section of the cylinder is rotated again to allow the water to flow through the space left by the slotted section of the cylinder. On the right of the picture is Mr R. Clayton, who was for many years the supply engineer for the Longdendale and Glossop Headworks.

Crowden Hall, 1937. The site is now used for camping. The former Tudor-style mansion was built in 1862 for the Hadfield family, who for over 150 years were regarded as the local squires of the Crowden area of Longdendale. During the mid-eighteenth century, a Thomas Hadfield was born. Legend has it that a local astrologer said to Thomas that: 'powerful fate's resistless hand shall seal your fate in Cumberland'. Thomas scorned the old man and later married the daughter of the Duke of Rutland. They lived in London and Thomas lived a riotous life from his partner's private income. On the death of his wife, Thomas soon found himself penniless and disowned by the Duke, who regarded Thomas as a bounder. On 23 September 1803, Thomas Hadfield was found guilty of forgery and fraud, and was hanged in Carlisle. The Hadfield family continued to live at Crowden Hall until the 1880s, when the family became extinct. Manchester Corporation demolished the hall in 1937.

The children generally arose with her, and after her other boy had gone to his work at the mill, she made a practice of going to bed again with the children for about an hour. She had done so on the previous Friday morning, and after rising a second time, she milked a cow and occupied herself with other work until between nine and ten o'clock. She then went to weed a patch of potatoes close by the house, leaving a fire burning, and the two children asleep in a bed which stood about a yard from the fire. She had been in the potato ground for about an hour, when she bethought herself of going home to the children, but on looking at the house, she saw that it was enveloped in smoke.

She unlocked the door and tried to go in for the children, but she was compelled to retreat, as the roof was falling in, and the place was in flames. Other Witnesses stated that they saw the fire, and went to the place, and one of them broke in through the lodgers' room, but could not render any service, as that part was on fire. The childrens' remains, which were found where the bed stood, were drawn from the burning ruins with a potato hoe, their bodies falling in pieces. The beds, furniture, clothes, and other contents of the house were consumed.

The jury returned a verdict of 'accidental death', stating at the same time, that there had been gross neglect, which had been the cause of the accident. The children were interred in one coffin the same evening.

Today, to remind us where the above incident occurred, a marker stone remains, built into the stone boundary wall on the reservoir side of the road, a mile outside Tintwistle.

The marker stone is inscribed: 'Burned down. Two children burnt to death aged 3 and 5 years.

Above: *The Market Stone set in the boundary wall outside Tintwhistle recalls a tragedy of 1854.*

Opposite: *Mr George Henry Hill, who was articled to Mr Bateman and who was later his assistant engineer on the Longdendale Reservoirs. It is ironic, perhaps, that Mr Hill was chosen in preference to Mr Bateman as chief engineer for the construction of the future Thirlmere supply in the Lake District. It must be borne in mind that Bateman was then sixty-seven years of age and had only recently recovered from a serious illness.*

17 August 1858

Bateman's relationship with his Waterworks Committee was not as perfect as some people imagine, for in February 1851 he claimed additional expenditure of 'upwards of £300'. The claim was not for his own extra labour and responsibility, but reimbursement for monies paid out from his own pocket for the salaries of extra staff. After demanding a full statement of the money spent which Bateman sent them, the Corporation ignored his claims.

Four years later Bateman again requested 'payment for salaries and other expenses close upon £1,000'. In May 1856 he suggested arbitration. Eight months later, with not even a reply from the Corporation, Bateman threatened to take his claim to 'an Arbitrator of the Corporation's choice'. He made it perfectly clear that he was no longer prepared to continue to be responsible for the day to day management of the Longdendale Works. He stated: 'I am desirous that my connection with them should cease or be placed on a more definite footing than it now exists'.

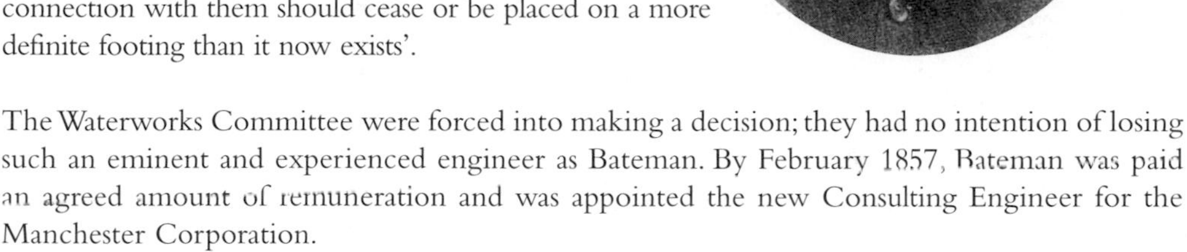

The Waterworks Committee were forced into making a decision; they had no intention of losing such an eminent and experienced engineer as Bateman. By February 1857, Bateman was paid an agreed amount of remuneration and was appointed the new Consulting Engineer for the Manchester Corporation.

Mr G.H. Hill shared the responsibility for the direct supervision of operations with Mr Wilson, the Outdoor Superintendent.

8 September 1857

Woodhead Reservoir,

In consequence of a telegram which I received on Thursday night in Scotland (Bateman's time and energy was also directed on the construction of the new Loch Katrine water supply for Glasgow) to the effect that a subsidence had taken place in the Woodhead Embankment, I came to Manchester by the next train and visited the place on Saturday morning. I found that what had occurred was nothing more than what I had anticipated would result from the boring which had recommenced. For some time the leakage has been occasionally discoloured and of course whenever this takes place, it arises from the wasting and carrying away of material. Although little in quantity, it produces hollows which eventually occasion settlements.

On the remainder of the works, I have nothing to say except that they are all in the most perfect and satisfactory state and order. Everything in his department reflects the greatest credit upon Mr Wilson, whose health, I regret to learn, has unfortunately suffered by unremitting attention to his duties.

Mr Wilson, the Outdoor Superintendent, who was heavily relied upon, both by Mr Bateman and Mr Hill, was absent through illness for a period of six months. He resided at Arnfield Towers, Tintwistle, a large, imposing house built and owned by the Manchester Corporation.

Arnfield Towers is now used as a private home for children with special needs.

9 January 1858

> The valley down which the water flows is but the main fissure of the district. It has been produced by an upward force and was originally but a crack in the crust of the earth, accompanied 'by an infinite number of minor parallel cracks, which, though not visible at the surface, extend longitudinally down both sides of the valley. In cutting the puddle trenches such longitudinal cracks were constantly discovered and crossed, and it was impossible in all cases to penetrate far enough into the hill to cut off all which could communicate in any way with the main valley which had subsequently to be filled with water. Another feature of the district was the multitude of landslips which had occurred from the gradual melting or perishing of the soft beds of shale and the falling of harder material which rested upon them and were thus undermined.
>
> Perhaps the experience I have now gained, and the eye I now claim to have for a land-slip, might enable me to detect difficulties which I could not then perceive.

Bateman had obviously been worried about the state of the Woodhead Reservoir embankment, and his immediate response to the telegram provides an indication of the importance he attached to this trouble-spot. After fourteen years of unease he finally decided to attempt to construct a completely new, additional embankment. His letter of 18 April 1860, confirmed his intentions.

Horse power from the magnificent Shire horses. The workforce muster behind loaded carts of railway sleepers. Horse-cart bodies are mounted onto railway-gauge wheels, with horses being used to haul the loads instead of a locomotive. The main works railway was a single-line track, which rules out the possibility that they were building that particular track. The location is probably Arnfield, where obviously a great deal of excavation was taking place.

16, George St. Westminster
18th April 1860

Dear Sir,
M.CWW.
I propose going over the Manchester Waterworks on Friday and Saturday next as I am anxious to see the Torside and Rhodes Wood Reservoirs.

I wrote to Mr Heron (Town Clerk) the other day asking if any of the Council would like to accompany me and whether the days I named would be convenient.

As I have not heard from him, he may be away from home, and I therefore write to ask you to be kind enough to ascertain how the matter stands and let me hear at Mr Fairbairns, at the Polygon tomorrow night. If I go by myself, or if you are good enough to accompany me, I will go in any way you think most convenient. Perhaps a Hansom Cab with a good horse from Greenwood's would be best. If you think so will you order one to be at Mr Fairbairn's at half past nine on Friday morning.

In haste.
Yours v. Truly,
(signed) J.F. Bateman.
Charles Wilson Esqr.

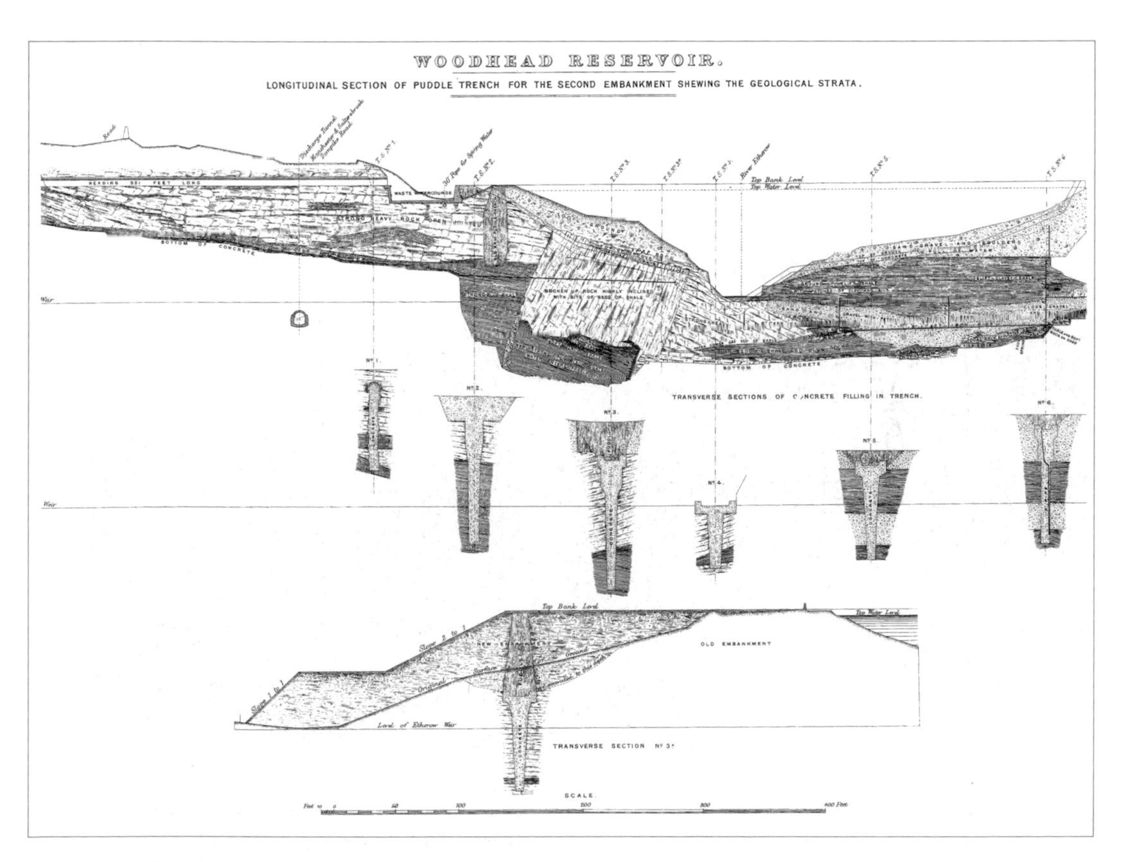

Plan of the longitudinal section of puddle trench for the second embankment, showing the geological strata, Woodhead Reservoir.

four

1862 – Labour Unrest, Second Embankment

A Second Embankment at Woodhead

The announcement the Committee were waiting for; Bateman finally makes his decision – a new Embankment at Woodhead, below the existing Embankment, which had caused Bateman so much concern and anxiety for the last fourteen years.

By careful boring, Bateman had at last discovered a continuous length of shale which existed right across the valley, from top water on one side to top water on the other, and at this spot a new embankment was to be formed.

It was imperative to make the valley sides watertight to well above the intended top water level, and to prevent leakage from occurring under the dam of the reservoir.

His intention was to leave the existing embankment (dam), then fill up the hollow between it and the new proposed embankment.

The new embankment would not interfere with the already constructed masonry overflow-weir or the flood water course.

11 September 1862

> I can with every confidence recommend the construction of a new Embankment below the present one, which when completed will enable the Reservoir to be filled to the brim and secure you one hundred million cubic feet of additional storage.
>
> The work will have to be carried out on land which does not belong to you and the puddle trench will have to pass under the Manchester to Sheffield Railway. It may be possible perhaps, to make arrangements with the parties interested, but if you have to go to Parliament for any other purpose, it would be desirable to include this Work, in order to obtain the necessary compulsory powers of purchase.
>
> Should an application to Parliament be determined, it might also be desirable to include the proposed Reservoir at Bottoms Lodge with the Works connected therewith.

Choking and boring had been an intricate part of the sealing process which Bateman had devised on his reservoirs, especially the Woodhead embankment. From some of the reports from Mr Wilson, the Outdoor Superintendent, we glean the following interesting facts:

The original office block was situated on the old Coach Road leading to the present NWW Department at Bottoms. It was demolished around 1905, when the new offices and workshops were built.

1 May 1862

Woodhead Reservoir – As proposed in my last report I have communicated with Mr Bateman, and in consequence of his instructions the bore hole in the embankment has been choked up. 87 harrows frill of ashes and about 1cwt of iron borings were used in choking it. The borers are all now at work in boring (in connection with the new embankment) at places pointed out by Mr Bateman.

6 March 1862

Woodhead Reservoir – I beg to report that the work connected with choking the leakage at the Woodhead embankment is in progress. I have prepared a tabulated statement, showing particulars of last fortnight's operations.

There are four men employed at the work, 2 at 4/-s and 2 at 3/-s per day – total 14/-s per day or £4-4s per week. In addition to these wages we shall have to pay the head borer 6d per yard for the net depth bored.

6 January 1864

Woodhead Reservoir – About three weeks ago the driving of the new discharge tunnel was obliged to be suspended by the eruption of water in such quantity as to produce drowning out of the workmen.

Mr Hill has furnished me with the fill particular of the occurrence and coupling the information thus obtained with that we previously possessed, it appears quite obvious that the tunnel has been driven to the top of the mass of retentive shale which had kept in the water, and that on the workmen breaking through this into the more open stratum of rock above, the water had immediately escaped into the tunnel.

With the information now before us it will be a better, safer, and cheaper plan to abandon this shaft, and sink another in place of it, below the intended new puddle trench, near the Northerly end of the present waste-weir.

5 July 1865

Presuming that you will be anxious to commence the execution of some of the Works for which you have recently obtained Parliamentary Powers, especially as the workmen superintended by Mr Taylor are now almost unemployed, we have prepared the working drawings for, and set out a considerable portion of those works which must be first executed at the Vale House Reservoir, on which the men could be immediately set to work if you sanction their proceeding. Among these works is the Road from Tintwistle to the Embankment of the intended Vale House Reservoir, and which should be immediately commenced, and proceeded with as rapidly as possible for the purpose of facilitating the delivery of stone and other material which may have to be bought from a distance. The making of this road, the sinking of a considerable portion of the puddle trench of the Bank, and the lining of the Discharge Tunnel may be proceeded with.

The commencement of the construction of Vale House Reservoir must have saddened many of the local population, especially the elderly.

The village population of Vale House was described in 1830 as 'amounting to some 600 souls'. This appeared in a small booklet dealing with the Wesleyan Methodist religion in Glossop-Dale, and it was primarily for these 600 people that the Tintwistle Ebenezer Methodist Chapel was built at that time.

Woodhead

May 14th 1862

Sir

The No 4 Bore Hole on the Cheshire side in the Feild Below the Woodhead Chapel Contains 5 feet of Red soil and stone and then Dry Shale 19 ft and then Stone 1 ft 7 inch and then Shale 6 in and then stone again 5 ft 11 inch and then soft Shale 1 ft 6 in and then stone 9 inch then Shale 2 inch then stone 11 inch Shale 4 inch and then stone 2 ft and then Shale 13 ft Tattal 50 ft 8 inches

and this Bore Hole is stoped for the Present

Left: *A typical example of the Mining Inspector's report.*

Below and opposite: *Vale House Mills, where woollen cloth manufacturing and cotton spinning took place. All buildings have been demolished and the site is now submerged in Vale House Reservoir.*

The Corporation, under the Act, were, of course, empowered to purchase the lands, and property, which would be submerged with the construction of the reservoir. In 1865, in addition to the Vale House Mill, there were over fifty properties close to the mill, including a gas works, cottages, shops, school house, and the manager's house, with a probable population of 400 to 500. Having bought the mill the Corporation sold the contents in 1867, and as the filling of the reservoir began in 1869, all the cottages would be vacated by that time.

There is no evidence of a mass exodus, or evacuation, of Vale House village. It is indeed quite possible that the abandonment of the village began much earlier. The Vale House Mill was constructed in 1775, and as more modern mills were built elsewhere, such as at Bridge Mill, Tintwistle, in 1854, and Waterside Mill, Hadfield, around 1828, workpeople were attracted by the prospects of larger incomes with the newer, faster machinery, and orders for the Vale House Mill declined. Indeed, in 1857, there was some unemployment. It is also probable that once the intention of the Corporation to submerge the village was known, probably by the early 1860s, the incentive to drift away would be increased. Other accommodation would be available in cottages built near the newer mills; nevertheless, many people must have been made bitterly disappointed and unhappy, all in the name of progress.

Both Vale House Reservoir and Bottoms Reservoir were planned to supply only the mills below with the statutory compensation water. These two reservoirs could not be used to supply drinking water, as they were constructed below the level which water could flow by gravity to Manchester and Salford, otherwise pumping would be necessary.

Meanwhile, while this work was advancing, a constant supply of water had to be maintained to the city of Manchester, together with a regular supply of compensation water to the mill owners.

Thus it was of the most paramount importance to maintain supplies at the Woodhead Reservoir, which was, at that time, the only guaranteed water available.

20 March 1866

On the 23rd of last month, I had the opportunity of examining the Works in Longdendale, and more particularly the puddle trench now sinking at the site of the Embankment for the Vale House Reservoir.

Across the greater part of the Valley it had been sunk to an average depth of about 35ft through a bed of hard rock, which I believe to be a seam distinguished by the name of 'Lower Millstone Grit', almost immediately beneath which occur the Limestone Shales so well developed at Mam Tor, near Castleton, in Derbyshire. The horizontal beds or partings of this rock are watertight, or nearly so, but there are numerous vertical fissures, some of which are open, allowing the pressure of water but most of which are filled with clay which has been gradually deposited from above, the deeper you go, the more completely are the fissures filled, and denser and firmer is the clay. We may therefore pretty confidentially rely upon obtaining a good watertight foundation in this rock.

7th June 1866

Death of Mr Samuel Taylor – Resident Inspector of Works.

The Outdoor Superintendent reports that Mr Samuel Taylor died on Sunday morning last. For a long time back, as the Committee are aware, he has been incapable from illness of doing anything but driving from his house to the Office at the Works and after remaining there a portion of the day returning home. On the 12th April he became so much worse as to be no longer able even to do this and I believe that with two or three exceptions he was never out of the house after that date. He suffered very much before he died and I believe his last words were 'Ah! This is not Corporation! This is a long journey!

Mr Samuel Taylor was first associated with the Longdendale Works when he was the Contractor for the Hollingworth and Arnfield Reservoirs. Some months after the completion of his Contracts (From Bateman's Report dated 19th March 1856), Mr Taylor was appointed Resident Inspector of Works, Longdendale, for the Manchester Waterworks.

30 November 1867

Vale House – A very satisfactory foundation has been found for the puddle of the Embankment of the Vale House Reservoir, the discharge tunnel has been completed, and the discharge-pipes introduced and fixed, the trough which carried the River over the puddle trench during the time it was being sunk has been removed, and reconstructed at a higher level, the embankment and puddle trench being also raised to a height.

At the Bottoms Reservoir, the discharge tunnel is now driven through and the lining with stone commenced. The puddle trench is sunk right across the Valley to rather more than its total depth.

The introduction of steam cranes and other arrangements for economising labour at this Reservoir have been very successful and beneficial, and great credit is due to those who have the immediate charge of the works for the manner in which every operation is performed.

At the pathways across the Weirs of the Residuum Lodges at the heads of the two arms of the Woodhead Reservoir, it will be desirable to place a hand-railing to prevent the danger of being blown over in strong wind. Hitherto these pathways have been unguarded, but the wind is sometimes so strong that the Reservoir Attendant has occasionally to crawl over on his hands and knees.

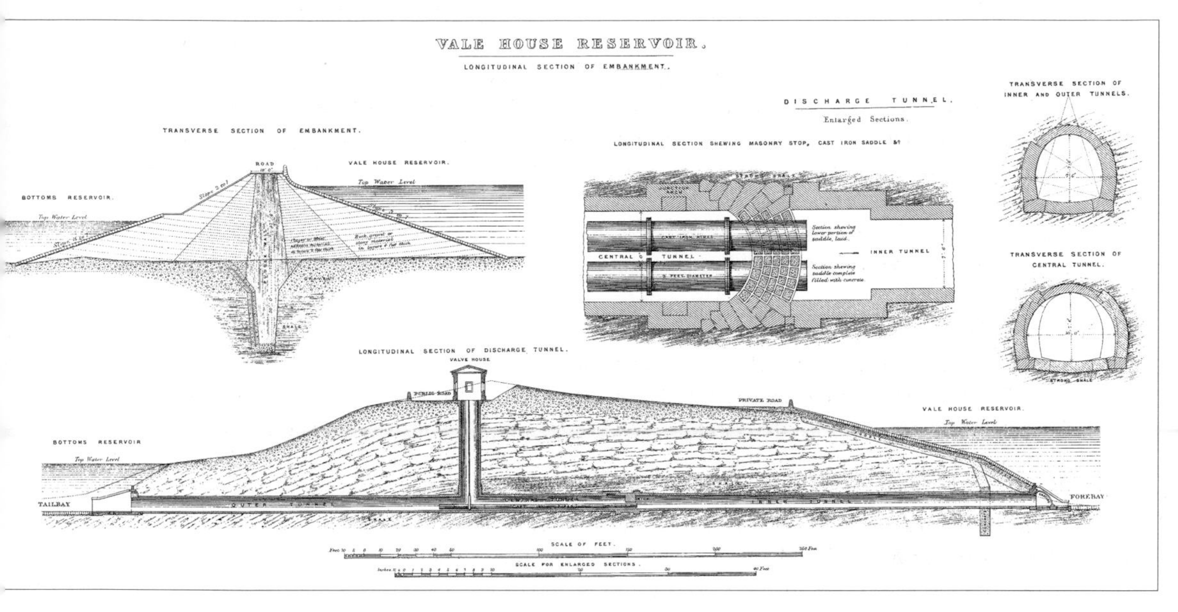

Drawing of the longitudinal section of the embankment at Vale House Reservoir.

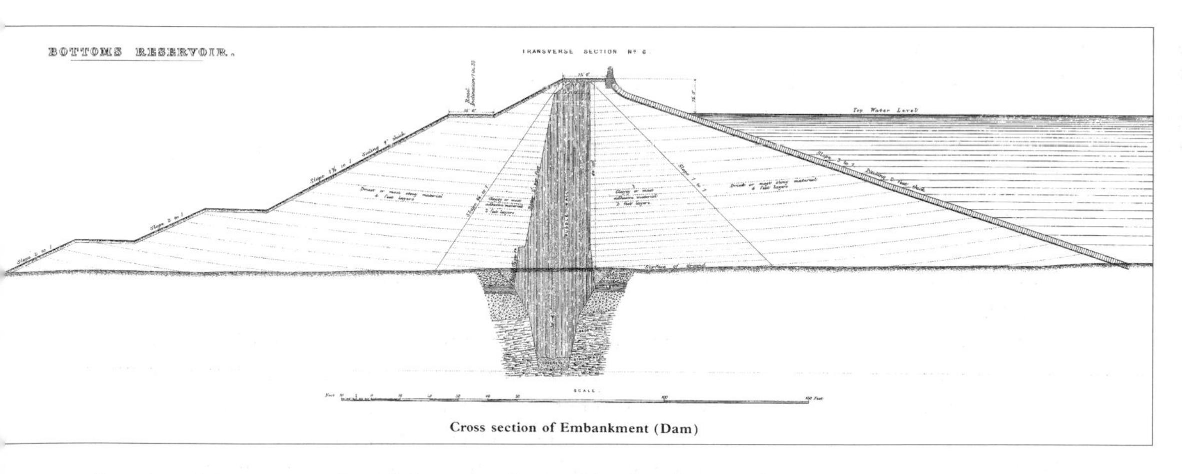

Cross section of Embankment (Dam)

Drawing of the cross-section of the embankment (dam) at Bottoms Reservoir.

The following extracts were taken from the Manchester Corporation Committee Proceedings which Mr Hill, Mr Bateman's assistant, reported to his Waterworks Committee, regarding labour relations during the construction of the Vale House and Bottoms Reservoirs.

23 April 1868

Labour troubles at Vale House and Bottoms Construction

The Outdoor Superintendent reports that there are two Inspectors or Foreman of Masons at Vale House and Bottoms Reservoirs viz., George Miller and John Bradbury who have applied for an increase to their wages which are at present 36/- per week. If the application be entertained it may be desirable to allow Miller 42/- and Bredbury 40/- per week. It is the duty of these men (under Dutton) to be constantly with the Masons to see that they do a full amount of work and to see that the stones are worked to their proper size and shape and correctly set.

The Outdoor Superintendent also reports that the Masons working at Vale House and Bottoms have sent the accompanying application for an advance of wages. If this application be entertained it may be desirable to fix the highest amount to be paid to the best Masons at 5/6 per day. The price at present is 5/- per day.

There is a large number of quarrymen or Stonegetters at work getting stone at the site of the Waste Weir or Overflow of the Vale House Reservoir who have been receiving 3/9 per day, but they have applied for increased wages and Dutton has been obliged to advance several of them to 4/- per day, and it is desirable to fix the highest amount to be paid to the best Stonegetters at 4/- per day.

The rate at which the Works at Vale House will progress entirely depends upon the stone getting and the masonwork. This is also true to a large extent as regards the work at Bottoms.

30 April 1868

Resolution of Waterworks Sub-Comittee on the above matter

The Works Sub-Committee report that they visited the Bottoms and Vale House Reservoirs and the Torside Waste Weir on Saturday last, the 25th instant, and that it appeared to them that the various works in progress were being carried out with care and expedition and that (considering the large amount of masonry required) they recommend the Committee to allow the masons to be paid as high a rate of wages as may be paid by other employers in the neighbourhood.

7 May 1868

Labour troubles at Vale House and Bottoms Reservoirs

The Outdoor Superintendent reports that the Masons at Vale House and Bottoms Reservoirs left their work on Friday morning last stating that they could not work any longer during the Summer for less than £1 13/- per week, being the Summer rate of stages fixed for the Glossop Branch of the Mason's Society. The Outdoor Superintendent (after consulting the Chairman) met adaptation from the Masons at Bottoms on the Friday evening and arranged with them that they should commence work on the Monday morning at the increased rate of wages for efficient works, and that the Waterworks Committee would determine today whether they should continue working at such increased rate or not.

The Outdoor Superintendent saw a deputation from the Masons again last night and informed them that if the Committee decided to pay the increased rate of wages that they would have to commence work at Bottoms and Vale House at 10 minutes past 6 o'clock for every morning except Monday, instead of half past six o'clock as at present?

Bottoms Quarry, Tintwhistle. The labour force in the quarry about that time was between thirty and forty men. Note the dressed masonry on the left of the picture, ready for delivery to the work site, c.1895.

Left: *Repairs to the pitching, Torside Reservoir embankment, c. 1890. These repairs were due to the installation of the new syphon valves. They were established in 1889, sixteen years after Bateman had first recommended their installation. The dressed stone would be bedded on an almost dry mix of concrete, covering the clay puddle blanket, which formed a watertight membrane on the inside of the reservoir embankment.*

Below: *Work completed on the Torside Reservoir embankment, c.1890. Note the valve syphons. In the case of Torside's syphon valves, there are two in number, one positioned at 25ft below top water level, and the other at 40ft below top water level. The photograph shows the head-stocks at the top of the inside of the embankment which, by manual control, open and close each of the valves. The water level in the picture would be approximately 15ft below the top water level of the reservoir.*

The first Bateman steam locomotives to run alongside the water reserves.

Once again, the dispute between the Manchester Corporation and their workforce was amicably resolved but, for some, there was sadness. The *Glossop Chronicle and Advertiser* reported that:

'On the 4th July 1868 James Nicholls was killed by a fall of earth. 400 navvies, in white smocks, walked at his funeral, and each gave 1 shilling towards the expense of the funeral and relief of his parents'.

4 May 1869

The number of men employed on the works is about 600.

3 October 1871

At the Torside Reservoir it was satisfactory to find that all the previous repairs were in perfect condition. We may probably venture to hold water in this Reservoir to top water level next Season.

This will make an important addition to the available storage particularly as the Bottoms Reservoir, though steadily advancing towards completion, cannot now be even partially filled with water till both it, and the Woodhead Embankment are completed, inasmuch as the Clay for the puddle walls of both Embankments has to be obtained from within the Basin of Bottoms Reservoir. The narrow gauge railway which has been laid for conveying this Clay to the Woodhead bank is working most satisfactorily, and is found in many ways a great advantage.

Great progress in the masonry on all parts of the Works have been made during the Summer, and the completed works are all in a satisfactory condition.

The Longdendale Works Railway to which Bateman had referred was another historical link in the construction and maintenance of the reservoirs and ancillary works.

In 1904 the steam locomotive was replaced by electric traction, the hydro-electric power being generated from Bottoms Reservoir.

The first railway-engine was steam-driven, running on a 3ft-gauge-track from Bottoms Dept to Woodhead, a distance of over four miles. It was used for carrying both men and materials. (See photograph on previous page).

In 1904 the steam-locomotive was replaced by an electric-traction, the power being supplied by a hydro-electric installation utilising the discharge of compensation water from Bottoms Reservoir. The electricity was also used for operating machine tools and so on at the Bottoms workshops (a brainchild of Bateman's many years earlier). The electric railway ran between Bottoms Dept and terminated at Crowden, the power being fed by way of an overhead trolley-wire. In 1938 the Power House at Bottoms was abandoned; a transformer and rectifier was installed, which allowed electricity to be supplied from the Stalybridge, Hyde, Mossley, and Dukinfield Joint Electricity Board.

A further alteration was made in the length of the railway-track in 1947, the journey being reduced to two and a half miles, between the Dept at Bottoms and Torside embankment.

The electric-locomotive was finally scrapped and the overhead trolley power line removed in 1950, but the age of the train was not yet over.

The railway continued, this time with a Ruston Hornby diesel locomotive, and gave sterling service to the works. But alas, in 1968 the railway was finally abandoned, and the railway track ripped up, much to the discordance of many, after ninety-seven years of continuous service.

13 June 1873

At Woodhead, the sinking and refilling of the puddle trench is making fair progress, the winding gear of the valves made by the Fairbarn Engineering Co., has been erected; but still requires bolting down to its foundation before it can be worked. When this is done, the water of the reservoir can be passed through the discharge tunnels. The temporary wooden trough in the centre of the bank may be removed, and the work at that point may be carried out more rapidly than has hitherto been possible.

Foundations for Bottoms overflow and waste weir, Bottoms Reservoir. Construction commenced in 1868. Woodhead Road, Tintwhistle, can be seen in the background.

Bottoms Reservoir Valve House. Bateman referred to this as 'An Ornamental Temple' (see page 83).

In consequence of the construction of the Vale House and Bottoms Reservoirs, the Torside Reservoir will now become a Reservoir for pure water for the service of the Town. The purest water in every Reservoir, lies within a few feet of the surface, and I have therefore to recommend, that, both at this Reservoir and at the Rhodes Wood Reservoir, arrangements should be made, by the introduction of syphon pipes over the bank, and down the inside slope, for drawing off water at several different levels to a depth of about 30 or 40 feet below top water level. This may be safely accomplished by sinking a pipe, 2 feet in diameter, to a depth of about 10 feet below the highest top water level and then carrying the short leg down the inner slope of the bank, with a valve at every 10 feet to admit the water at various levels, and the long leg to the bottom of the embankment on the outside, with a valve at the bottom to command its discharge into the watercourse by which the water may be conveyed to Manchester.

From the proceedings of the Waterworks Committee dated 12 February 1874, we learn of the arrangements desirable in consequence of the death of Mr Charles Wilson, Outdoor Superintendent, 'recommending the appointment of Mr G.H. Hill, C. Eng. to take charge of the Reservoirs and Works in connection therewith until completed with other duties, in consideration of a remuneration of £350 per annum.'

6 October 1874

The domestic habits of the people are undergoing great changes, by the freer use of water for the purposes of ablution, and by the introduction of water closets and baths, while at the same time, greater use is made by the residents in the suburbs, who not only use water for ordinary domestic purpose but for stables, cattle, and gardens, all of which may be considered legitimate purposes and of which the supply of water to a town should be employed.

The second Woodhead embankment or dam under construction. The original overflow weir, which was constructed for the first embankment and re-used for the second, can be seen at the top left of the picture. The entrance to the new discharge tunnel can be seen in the middle on the left. Between the discharge tunnel and the Millowners Watercourse, at the lower left of the picture, the Residuum Lodge, later known as the Etherow Pool, is also under construction (see plan of the embankment or dam on page 36). Note the large stack of dressed masonry, ready for use in building the Etherow Pool. Many of the photographs recording the progress of the works were taken by a famous Victorian photographer of the day, Mr J. Mudd.

From his book, *The History of the Manchester Waterworks*, Bateman sadly informs us, 'In July 1875, I was taken ill and did not attend to business till midsummer, 1876.'

April 1876 – Valve House at Bottoms Reservoir – Mr Hill's Repo

The Masonry of this Valve House is in progress, and I now beg to lay bef es of the Tablets proposed to be inserted in the walls.

One Tablet is intended to be of granite, and to be placed on the outside he side walls (see photograph, page 81). This Tablet is shown on the Sketch Tra and the inscription describes shortly the Acts under which the Works have been continued, with the names of the Chairman and Deputy Chairman of the Committees. The other Tablet will be of Marble, and is to be placed on the inside of one of the walls of the Valve House. This Tablet is shown on Sketch No.2, and contains the names of all gentlemen who have acted on the Water Committee since the year 1846.

The work had been carefully considered by Mr Bateman before his illness, and as the Valve House is now in progress, I shall be obliged by your instructions to carry out the design. Mr Bateman has consulted Mr Carson, the Architect, as to the Tablets, and would be glad to have his assistance in the preparation of them.

And so we come to Bateman's final report on the completion of the Longdendale Reservoirs after thirty years of trials, tribulations and ultimate success.

16 Great George Street, Westminster S.W.

7 February 1877

Manchester Corporation Waterworks

To the Water Committee,

Gentlemen,

It is with unusual gratification that I am now to report an examination which I made of the works in Longdendale on the 31st ultimo.

The whole of the works in that valley may now be said to be substantially completed.

The Woodhead Reservoir, had for the first time, run over the Waste Weir on the 14th of January, and was running over on the day of my visit.

Thus, was safely brought to a termination, the labour and anxiety of nearly a third of a century, for the works at the Woodhead Reservoir commenced in August 1848.

It is thus 13 years since the Embankment, which has been so successfully completed, was determined upon.

In order that you may understand. the difficulties which had been surmounted, I hand you a Geological Section of the puddle trench of the new Embankment, from which you will see the various dislocated strata we had to contend with, and that the new puddle trench has been sunk about 160 feet below the top of the old Embankment, and for nearly the whole of this depth, through solid rock. It was also sunk between 50 and 60 feet below the old River course in the centre of the valley, and about 100 feet below the Sheffield and Manchester Railway.

No clay puddle, no matter how thick, or how well made could have stood the wasting or penetrating power of 160 feet of water. The trench, therefore was filled with hydraulic concrete, wherever water could reach it through the fissures of the rock, to prevent escape from the Reservoir.

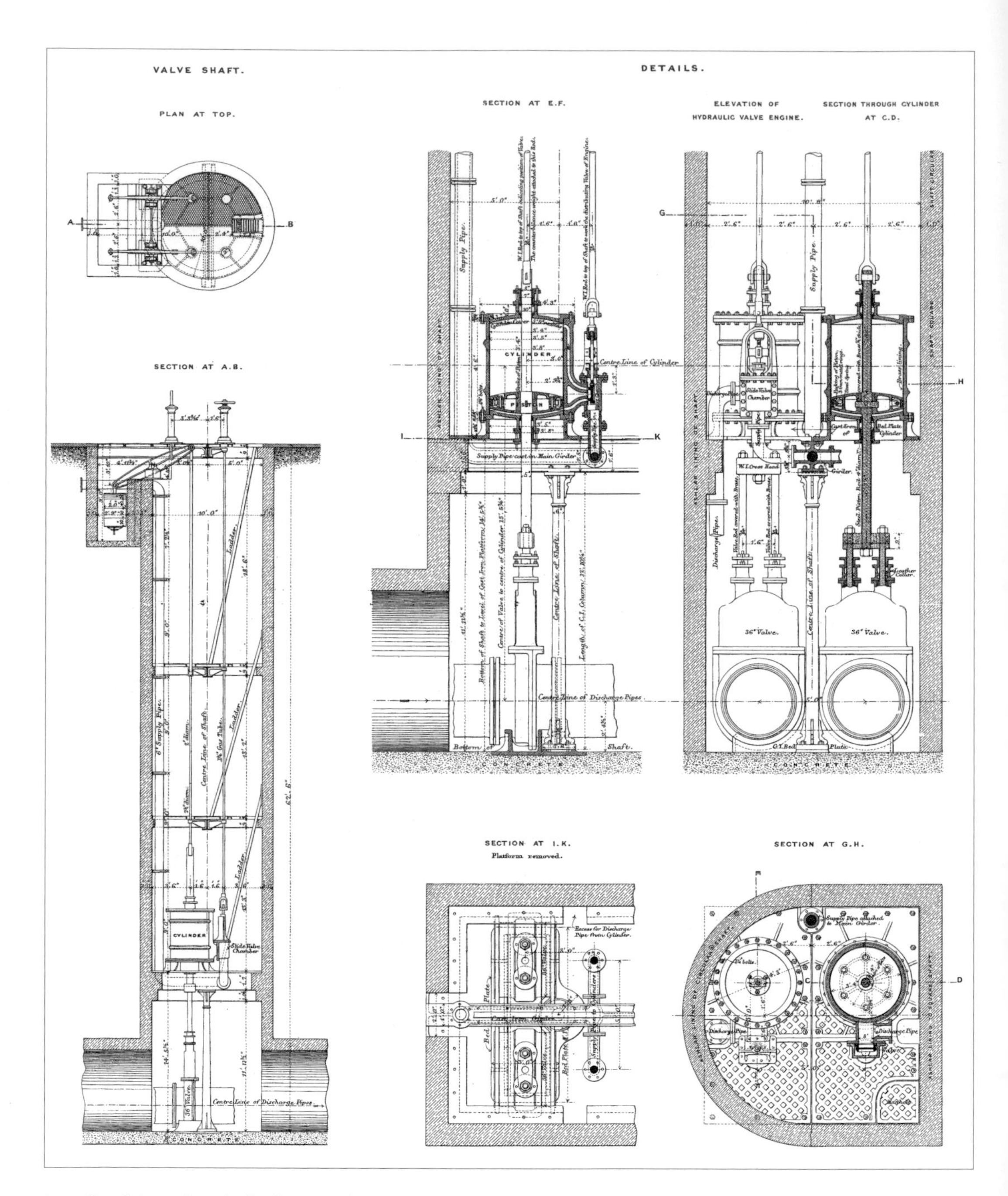

Details of the valve shaft, showing the arrangement of hydraulic engines for working valves, Bottoms Reservoir.

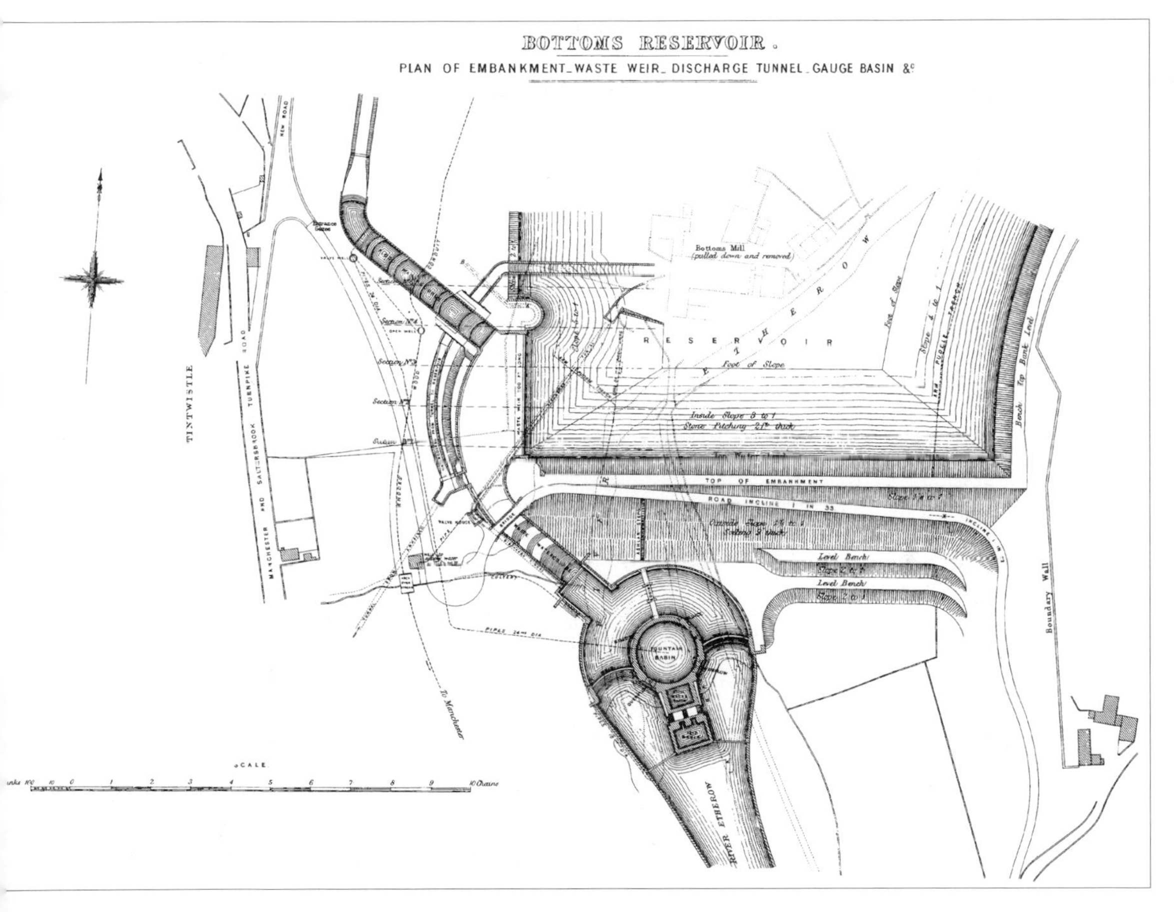

Plan of the embankment, waste weir, discharge tunnel and gauge basin, Bottoms Reservoir.

Millowners gauging basin and waste weirs under construction, Bottoms Reservoir, 1870. In the background, Bottoms Reservoir embankment can also be seen under construction. In their lust for profit, the efficiency of the Millowners was without doubt. To ensure that they obtained every drop of water that was due to them, they insisted on a gauge being provided, in which they filled a tank of water at a certain time, and together with a secret depth gauge, they could check whether the flow of water was correct. Heavy penalties were provided for failure to discharge the specified amounts, for in 1848 they were allowed a maximum of 121 million gallons per week. The Act of 1854 fixed this amount to the present rate of 70 million gallons per week. But in the old days, a ritual was observed by the Millowners' representative and the reservoir keeper of Bottoms. At 6 a.m. every working day, they would check the gauge. Today, water is as precious to the industrialists as it was back in the days of the Industrial Revolution.

Hollins Weir, Rhodeswood.

The Torside Reservoir has also given us much anxiety and trouble, but this also, I am happy to say was full to within nine inches on the occasion of my visit.

Everything here, also, was in the most perfect and satisfactory condition.

The Rhodeswood Reservoir, and the Vale House Reservoir, were full of water and running over. The Bottoms Reservoir, the last of the series; was full to the level of the present height of the waste weir, which is seven feet below that contemplated, and in anticipation of which, the Bank across the valley and the arm puddle trench on the south side have been constructed.

I am thus able, for the first time, to report the completion of all the works in Longdendale, and I have to thank the Corporation for their continued confidence in me during so long a period.

I laid out the first project for obtaining water from that district for the old Manchester and Salford Water Company in the year 1844. At that time, the population of Manchester and Salford was about 320,000 persons.

The population now dependent on the Corporation is about 760,000 persons.

Thirty years ago, the mechanical contrivances of water-works were in a very rude condition.

Nothing could be ruder, nor more discreditable to the mechanical skill of Waterworks Engineers, than the old wooden plug, which constituted the only means of obtaining water from street pipes in times of fire. The improvement of these arrangements was kept constantly before all my own Assistants and the mechanical men with whom I had to come in contact.

This ended in the adoption of a Ball Valve, called a Hydrant or Fire Cock, the original idea of which was due to one of my own Assistants (Mr Moore) improved by myself, and bearing the name of 'Bateman and Moore's Fire Cock'.

By a Stand Pipe, capable of being easily carried by hand, which communicated with these Cocks, they could be instantly opened and attached to hose through which a jet of water could be thrown from the Street main to the top of the highest building.

When the water was first supplied to Manchester, Fire Engines were almost dispensed with, except as omnibuses to carry firemen and apparatus, and there is not a block of valuable buildings in the centre of Manchester, which is not commanded by from 50 to 100 fire cocks within 100 yards.

Although these Cocks had been tried at other places, previous to the construction of the Manchester Waterworks, yet it was here that they were first adopted to any great extent, and their successful application proved.

One beautiful arrangement, the suggestion of Mr Moore, has been adopted with reference to every stream in the district from which the water is collected. In its ordinary condition and in seasons of drought, the water yielded by every stream is spring water of the finest quality, but, on the occasion of sudden rain or long continued wet weather, the stream becomes swollen and turbid.

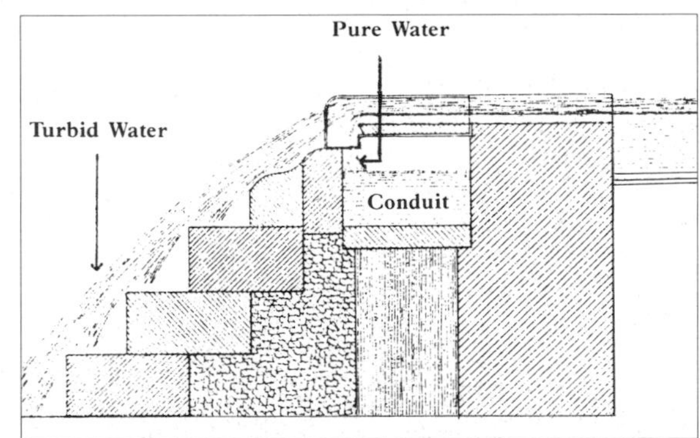

Cross-section of Hollins Weir.

When the stream is small, it drops over the edge of a weir with a small parabolic curve, and when swollen, it describes a larger curve, the water being projected forwards a considerable distance, more or less according to the volume of the stream, beyond the edge of the weir. (See photograph and cross-section of Hollins Weir, pages 86-87). Taking advantage of these circumstances, the pure water is allowed to fall into a slot in front of the weir, and, by means of a Conduit underneath the top, is conveyed direct to Manchester. When sudden rain swells the volume and occasions discolouration, the water is projected over this slot, not a drop entering it, and passes on to Reservoirs set apart for the storage of turbid water.

The arrangement is self-acting, never gets out of order, and never fails in performing its work.

In this way, all the pure water is reserved for the supply of Manchester, and the turbid water either set apart for the compensation water required to be delivered to the River, or used for Manchester, after exposure and precipitation.

Watercourses for floods, for compensation water and for pure water have been constructed so as to give you entire command of all the water of the district and gauges have been erected below every Reservoir, and in the watercourses, so as to enable you to ascertain exactly the quantity of water received from each Reservoir and delivered to the City of Manchester.

The capacities of each Reservoir have been determined, for every foot in depth in the larger Reservoirs, and for every inch in depth in the Service Reservoirs.

The City is supplied under 'Constant Supply' with probably the largest quantity of water of any large Waterworks in the Kingdom.

Of late years, other duties have called me away from Manchester, but my direct personal inspection has been ably supplied by Mr Hill.

One great advantage, which, in their wisdom, the Corporation adopted, has been the unlimited compulsory rate, which has enabled them to borrow money for the execution of the works, upon the lowest attainable interest.

The quantity of the water is such that upon the most undeniable statistics, the saving to the people now supplied with it, betwixt what they get and what they had from the Old Company, and could possibly get from wells and from the new red sandstone cannot be estimated at less than £100,000 a year, and I cannot but congratulate the Corporation of Manchester, not only upon the completion of the works with which I am more personally connected, but upon the wisdom which has been displayed by them in every step they have taken and every decision they have come to.

I must apologise for giving this short description of the works and a Summary of the various improvements which have been introduced in the course of their execution, but, so great is the benefit which you have conferred on the community, and so much has it contributed to the prosperity of the district, that I thought I might be well excused for thus shortly drawing your attention to the origin and history of the undertaking, and of the improvements in Water Supply which have been effected.

I have the honour to remain,

Gentlemen,
Your obedient servant.
J. Fred Bateman.

The construction of the service reservoirs at Audenshaw in 1884 signalled the final completion of the Longdendale Reservoirs Supply Scheme.

Above: *Gauge basin under construction, Bottoms Reservoir, 1870. The discharge tunnel which carries the compensation and scour pipes from the reservoir is on the right. Christ Church, Tintwhistle and the village can be seen in the background*

Right: *The Power House, downstream of Bottoms Reservoir, capable of producing a uniform supply of 360hp. It was abandoned as a power house in 1950, on termination of the works railway electric train.*

View of the gauge basin and river from Bottoms embankment, looking downstream in a south-west direction towards Tintwhistle Bridge. The remains of Bridge Mill are visible in the centre in the background.

Opposite: Sections of the valve shaft and valve house, Woodhead Reservoir.

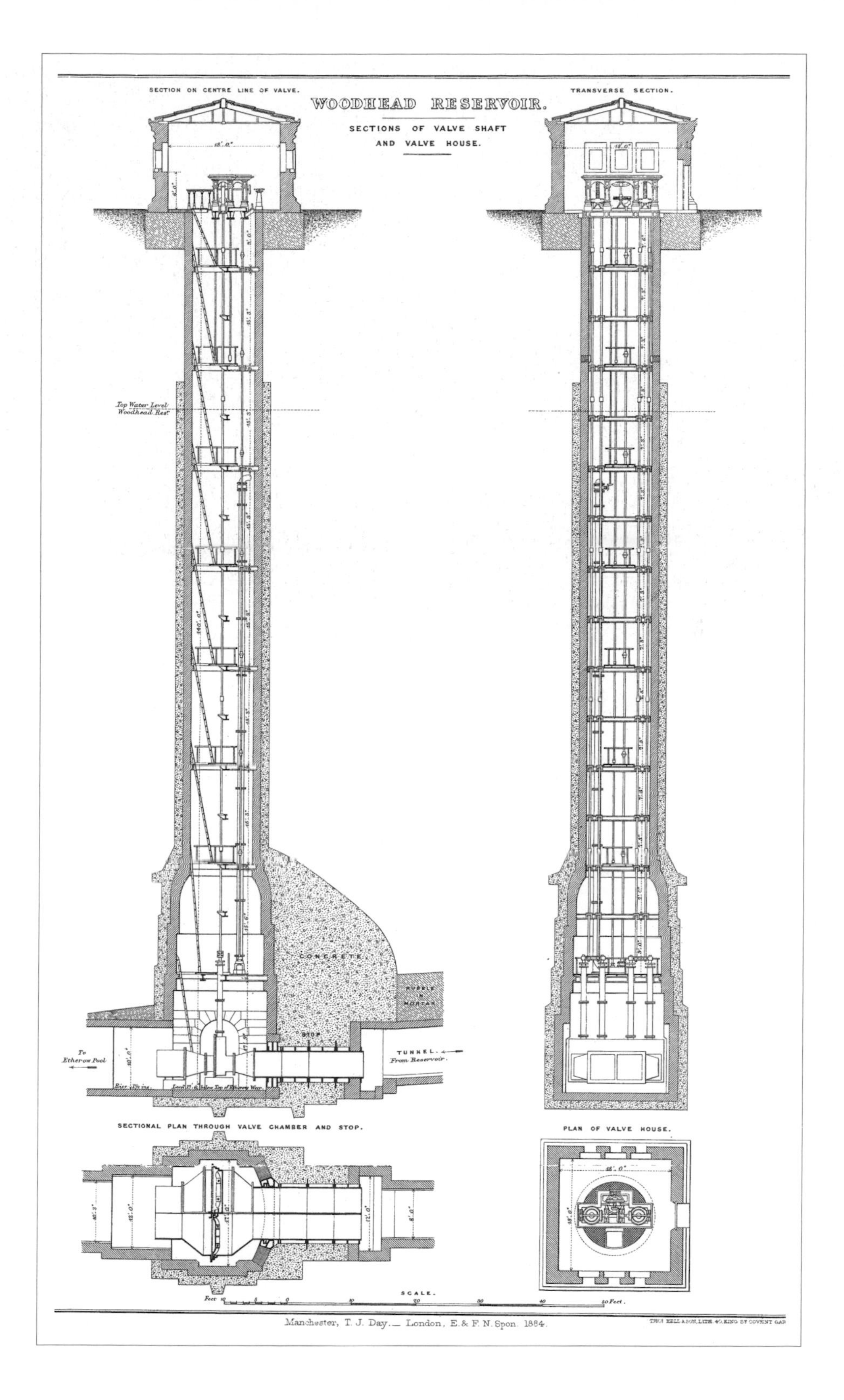
SECTION ON CENTRE LINE OF VALVE.
WOODHEAD RESERVOIR.
SECTIONS OF VALVE SHAFT
AND VALVE HOUSE.
TRANSVERSE SECTION.
Top Water Level
Woodhead Resr.
CONCRETE.
RUBBLE IN MORTAR
STOP
To
Etherow Pool
TUNNEL.
From Reservoir.
SECTIONAL PLAN THROUGH VALVE CHAMBER AND STOP.
PLAN OF VALVE HOUSE.
SCALE.
Feet
50 Feet.
Manchester, T. J. Day. _ London, E. & F. N. Spon. 1884.

five

What's Changed?

Today

Time waits for no man, so what has changed in the last 100 years? Groomsmen once washed down their coaches and stables; today drivers wash their cars. On warm Saturdays and Sundays, people still water their gardens. Housewives will be doing their washing on the coldest of weekends, but not perhaps on the traditional Monday morning of long ago. At breakfast-time, dinner-time, or tea-time, or when someone jumps up between advertisements on the 'telly' to make a 'cuppa', one thing is certain – water in the Service Reservoirs is being drawn down.

And as 100 years ago, the call will be for more water, and the reservoir keeper will trundle off to the Rhodeswood Valve House to open the supply valve to increase the demand for a further supply of pure water.

But for how long in this, the age of the microchip? The steam engine came and went, leaving black smoky dry-stone walls; the plodding horses have been replaced by Land Rovers; white canvas billow across Torside Reservoir; the Commodore fires his cannon; fishermen gather beside the waters of Vale House and tell about the one that got away.

Down the valley, marching like giant soldiers, are the CEGB electricity pylons, erected in 1965 as an unwanted necessity, and rubber stamped by an unwilling Peak Park Joint Planning Board.

On 1 April 1974, the pioneering Manchester Corporation Waterworks was swallowed up by the North West Water Authority.

In 1847, the Manchester Corporation purchased the Manchester & Salford Waterworks Co.'s undertaking for around £50,000 – what price privatisation?

Over at Arnfield, there has been one notable change. The Hollingworth Reservoir, which had for over sixty years been used for fish breeding, boasting its own Fish Hatchery, is no more. The water from Ogden Brook, which once supplied this reservoir, is now diverted into Arnfield

A photograph of the 'Waterworks Committee', probably taken to commemorate the official completion of the Longdendale Works in 1877. The location is possibly the Arnfield Brook vicinity.

Opposite page: *Helicopter power, the modern method of moving materials to remote sites.*

Reservoir if required, or sent down the flood tunnel and into Bottoms Compensation Reservoir. The Hollingworth Reservoir embankment had been constructed entirely of local clay, as Bateman had claimed that clay was the only material available in the immediate neighbourhood. During construction of the dam, the work had to be suspended many times because of the tendency for the clay to slump or slip. For many years, as a consequence of an historic landslip, the embankment had been constantly monitored for settlement and deterioration. In 1985, the fate of this reservoir was decided. It was emptied, demolished and landscaped. The full circle had been completed.

Everything and everybody has to move with the times, of course. Occasionally a helicopter will be used to transport materials and pipes across the twenty-six sq. miles of gathering grounds. Rainfall still piles up at an average of 52 ½in per year, and who will argue at the holding capacity of approximately 3,800 million gallons, together with the three open storage reservoirs of 1,500 million gallons at Audenshaw, which provide a safe, reliable yield for drinking water purposes of about 24 million gallons per day – give or take a pint or two.

All this after allowing for 10 million gallons per day compensation water, discharged into the river Etherow to keep its bed clean and to encourage fish and wildlife. Pounding the years, the Headworks system effectively controls the movement of water between the reservoirs, and ensures their safety during times of flooding.

Against time, water engineers have constantly strived to improve and modify the system, and a giant stride among these has been the provision of treatment works at Arnfield, Godley and Denton. Water is drawn from Rhodeswood Reservoir and is augmented by a supply from Arnfield Reservoir, and conveyed by a covered watercourse and pipeline to the Arnfield Sedimentation Plant, where suspended and colloidal matter is removed (or to put it another way, the mucky water is made nice and clean). From Arnfield, the water is passed to Godley Filtration Plant via a covered aqueduct, pipeline, and the Mottram Tunnel. At Godley, the greater part of the water is filtered and sterilised before passing into supply through the covered Godley Service Reservoir. The remainder of the water is either stored in Godley Open Service Reservoir or transferred to the open reservoirs at Audenshaw, for final treatment at the Denton plant. Regular scientific checks on water quality before, during and after treatment are made at the modern laboratories at Denton.

Because of new stringent safety conditions brought about under the Reservoirs Act of 1975, the Water Authority is required to increase the safety provisions of the Longdendale Reservoirs.

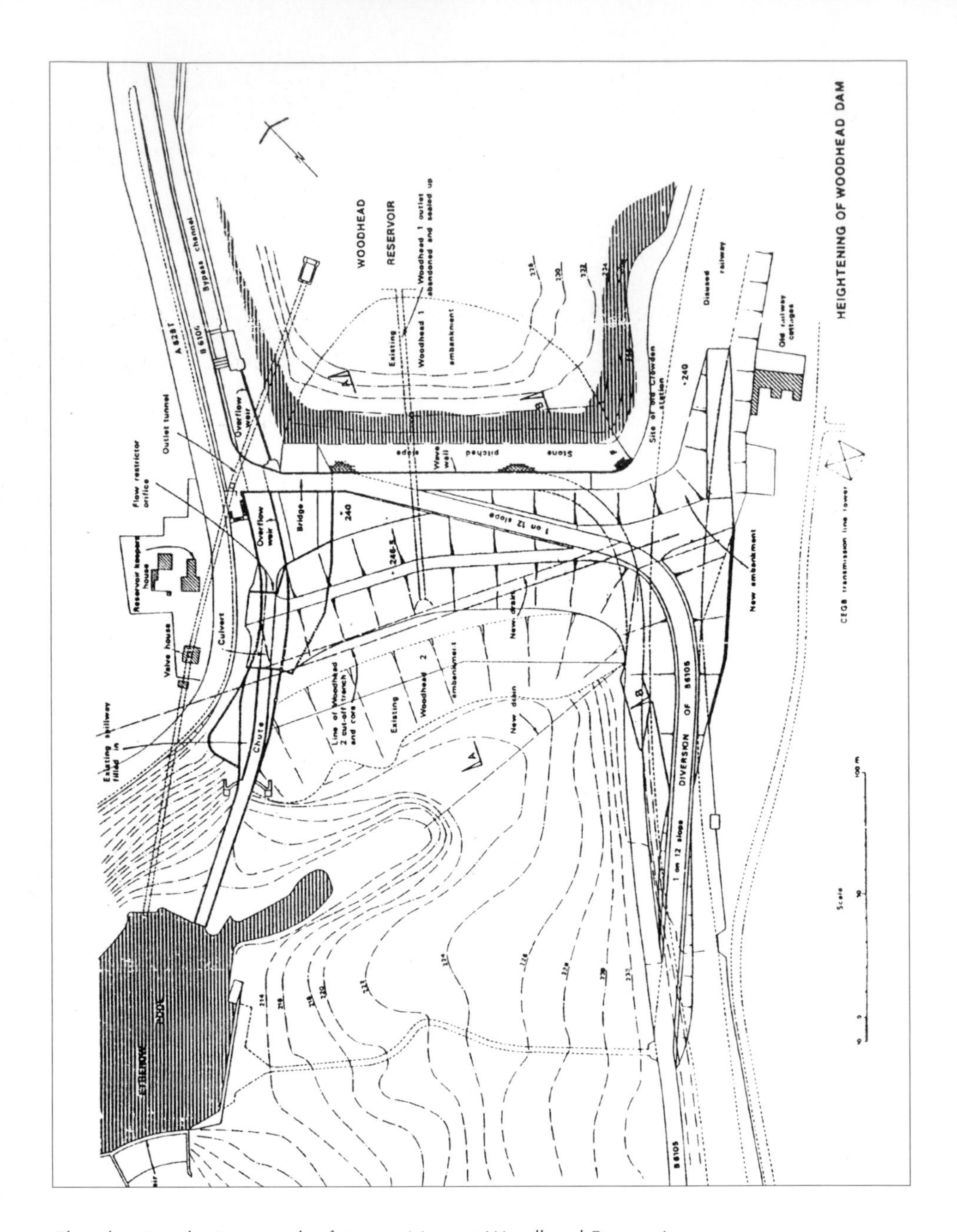

Plan showing the increased safety provisions at Woodhead Reservoir.

Nine alternative civil engineering concepts for achieving these provisions were proposed, and after much deliberation it was decided to increase the flood storage capacity of Woodhead Reservoir, which would diminish the requirements for structural changes in Torside, Rhodeswood, Vale House and Bottoms Reservoir.

In essence, it will mean increasing the height of the Woodhead dam by 6.7m to withstand a condition known as the Probable Maximum Flood (PMF).

It will also necessitate a realignment of the existing B6105 road to cross over the new embankment (see page 109).

The magnificent masonry edifices of the Victorian engineering structures must remain at all costs, and must never be replaced by concrete, plastic or other man-made materials.

Our heritage was built by men of vision, and is more important than the whims of some present-day engineers or the dictates of the whiz-kid economists.

Like rubies set in gold, so the cold, sad splendour of the masonry was set in the reservoirs in the hills, with the sweat and skill and cheap labour of our forefathers. If they were ever demolished they would be stricken from our history and lost forever.

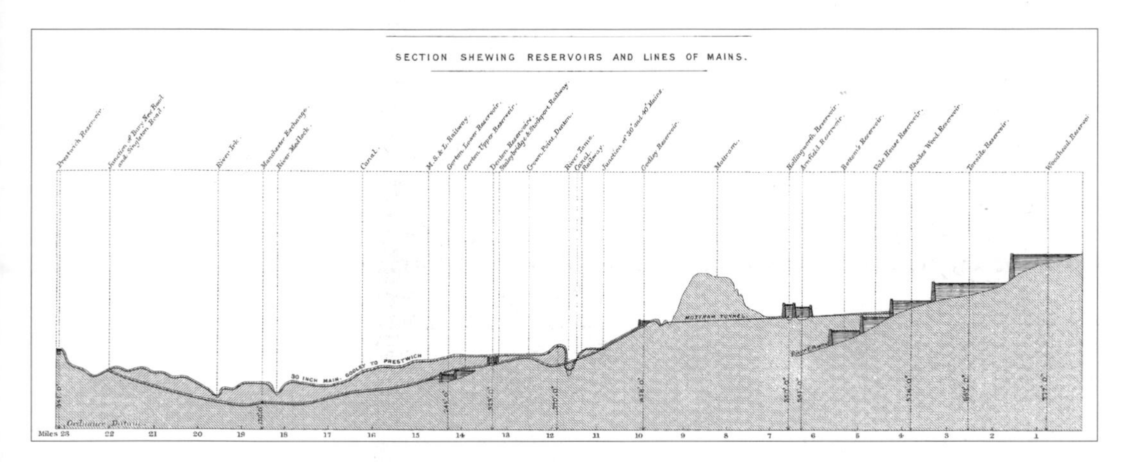

Section showing reservoirs and lines of mains.

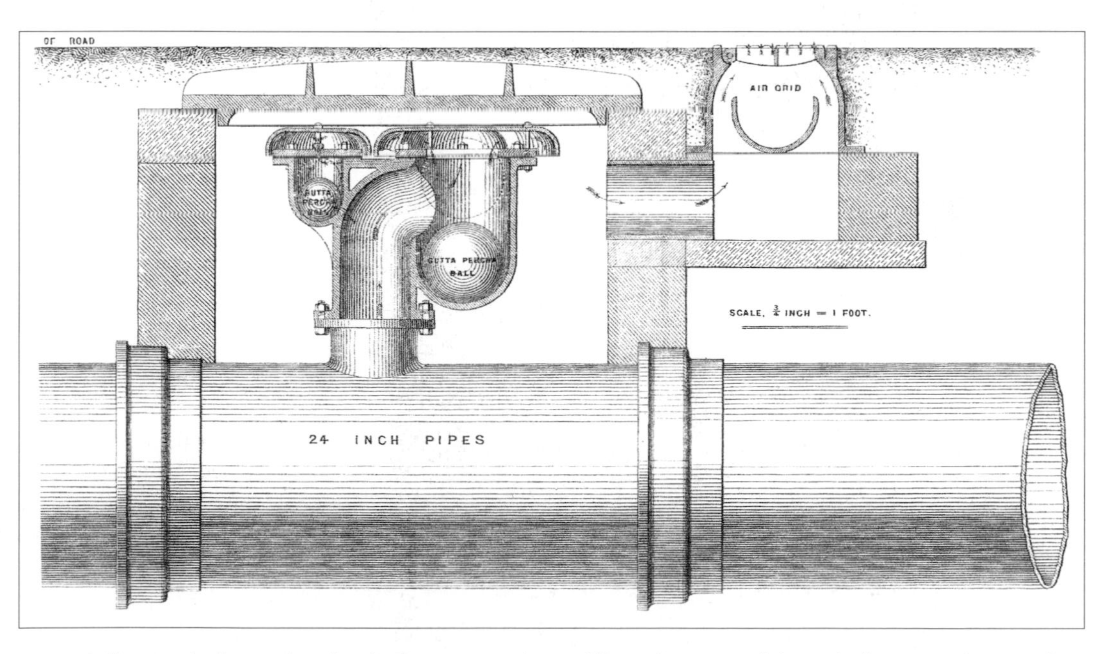

Self acting ball air valves for discharging air during filling of pipes, and that which accumulates under pressure when the pipes are filled with water.

six

History Revisited

Linking History and Reorganisation through the Years

John Frederick La Trobe Bateman, FRSS, L&E, Past President of the Inst. CE, FGS, ERGS, etc., – Pioneer, Water Engineer Extraordinaire – was proud of the unshakeable confidence the Manchester Corporation Waterworks had in him, for designing, constructing, and completing this great achievement of the Longdendale Reservoirs, which had taken over forty years of his life to complete, but he was also proud, using his own words, 'that I have been mainly instrumental in conferring on the inhabitants of Manchester and the neighbourhood, one of the greatest blessings which is possible for a town to enjoy'.

John Frederick Bateman began writing the first, or Historic Part, of his book, *History and Description of the Manchester Waterworks* whilst in Scotland midst a period of enforced leisure during December 1858 and January 1859, and although not completed until 25 years later, this mine of information was thankfully published in 1884. The 291-page volume, plus beautifully crafted drawings and diagrams, many of which I have proudly copied from his book as a living testament to his eye for detail, is for anybody thirsting for the history of Manchester's waterworks and for professional civil water engineers searching for knowledge on the historic construction of the Longdendale Valley Reservoirs.

In the opening paragraph of his book, we read:

> The city of Manchester has arisen upon and around the site of the old Roman station of Mancunium, near the confluence of several rivers and streams of water which take their rise in the high lands to the east and north-east of the city, descend through what was formally well wooded and picturesque valleys but which are now for the most part filled with towns, villages, mills and all the busy manufacturing establishments which are connected with the great seat of cotton trade of England. A well watered place it must have been in former times. The Irwell, the Medlock, the Irk and various streams, all abounding with fish, were never-failing sources of excellent water. The superficial beds of drift sand and gravel yielded copious springs, and the new red sandstone rock which lay beneath the town contained an almost inexhaustible supply of pleasant though hard, well-water. There was enough and more than enough for all the ordinary wants of a large population, and not until the streams were fouled by manufactories, and the sands and gravels covered by buildings, and the water they contained drained off or spoiled by the attendant operations, was it necessary to resort to artificial means for a water supply. Hence beyond here and there, a discovery of an ancient Roman British well, there are no early records or remains of any means for supplying the town with water.

From old records of the Manchester Court Leet, a former manorial court in England, we learn that there was one principal spring or fountain, rising in what is Manchester's city centre, and from which the name Fountain Street derived its name, now a bustling busy street during business hours. So from humble beginnings in 1505, Manchester's inhabitants drew their water from the spring or fountain which was conveyed by a conduit to what was once Market Place (see engraving on page 13), now part of Victoria Street.

In October of 1578, the Leet Jury, ordered that 'no person shall take water from the conduit, (term for the fountain) in any vessel of greater value, than one woman is able to bear filled with water, and but one of every house at one time, and have their call (or turn) as hath accustomed'. Officers were appointed to ensure the order was enforced. From this it would appear that a woman may have had to queue for hours in line to take her turn, on the condition that no family would be allowed more than four or five gallons per day.

By 1776 the fountain was beginning to diminish, with signs of the conduit running dry. Manchester was becoming a large town, with an ever-expanding population, resulting in more and more hand-operated water pumps appearing causing a reawakening in the demand for an improved water supply. The birth of reorganisation in the water industry surely had begun when the Lord of the Manor, Sir Oswald Mosley, embarked on his own waterworks company when he established a supply of pumped water, 'for raising water from the River Medlock at a short distance above the town'. The water was pumped to the higher parts of the town then stored in pits and ponds before being distributed to the lower areas; later it was found to be impure and unfit for domestic use. Additional water was supplied from bore holes sunk into the hard red sandstone.

An abundant supply of water had become an urgent priority for the town with the quarry owners, cotton masters, and the manufacturers requiring more water for production in their mills and factories. By 1808, the Manchester and Salford Waterworks Company had prepared two schemes for supplying the town, relying on water being extracted from the Rivers Medlock and Irk, the intention being to put the scheme forward before the next session of Parliament.

A public meeting was called in November 1808, where a debate ensued and a proposal was put forward for town ownership which was rejected, and in consequence a Committee was appointed to explore the possibilities of these two schemes. In February 1809 the committee reported back, criticising the adventurers who had suggested the two schemes and that in their opinion the supply of water would be insufficient for the supply of water for Manchester and that: 'the application thereof would be highly dangerous to private property, inasmuch as the same would cut off many springs and feeders which now supply large and extensive printing, bleaching and dyeworks with water, and afford to numerous cotton factories and other works condensing water for their steam engines.' They added that Manchester water ought to be under the direction of its own in habitants rather than water companies and put forward other sensible alternatives to supply water for the benefit of the people of Manchester.

Regretfully, the efforts of the town were unsuccessful and although they strenuously opposed the two schemes being put forward to Parliament, one of the companies, commonly called the Stone-Pipe Company, but properly named the Manchester and Salford Waterworks Company, succeeded in carrying their Bill, with ulterior motives in mind. The Stone-Pipe Company acted under the authority of a patent granted to Sir George Wright, baronet, of Ray Lodge, in the county of Essex in 1805, for, 'cutting pillars or tubes out of solid wood or stone'. (See page 18, the photograph taken at Arnfield Towers where the actual wood and stone-pipes were on display, excavated from the Manchester town distribution system of 1815.) To put the Manchester and Salford Waterworks Company on a sound footing and to prevent competition, they agreed with the Lord of the Manor, Sir Oswald Mosley, for the purchase of his interest in the waterworks, which then existed on a yearly rent of £624 10*s* 1*d*. On 20 June 1809 these two companies were legally formed to perpetuate one of the most barefaced and nefarious pieces of jobbery which has ever disgraced the annals of private companies – the Great Stone-Pipe Robbery, as mentioned earlier.

For many years the shareholders of the waterworks company and the town of Manchester and its inhabitants were, by trickery and devious management, secretly led by the Stone-Pipe Company for its own prosperity, fooled into thinking that the wellbeing of the people was being cared for. By 1815 the Great Stone-Pipe Company Fraud had been revealed, leaving the Manchester and Salford Waterworks Company in a deplorable state. The labourers and workforce wages were unpaid, no firm would sell anything to the company on credit, and Sir Oswald Mosley was screaming his head off for money still owing. A public outcry, ably supported by the townsmen of influence, prompted a call for new directors, who this time had to be actual residents of Manchester and not business men from out of town. The newly directed Manchester and Salford Waterworks Company even appointed trustees, who were responsible for the collection of water charges and delegated with the task of raising money to relay the failed stone pipes with a distribution network system of cast iron ones.

The company went on to supply water from streams outside the town which were relatively free of pollution, they built service reservoirs and sank deep wells, pumped by powerful engines and capable of delivering drinkable water throughout the town. People at least shared a tap with neighbours in the courtyard of the sordid dwellings in which they lived, but it was not uncommon for water to be contaminated, resulting in cholera and death. A clearer understanding between the Manchester Corporation and the Manchester and Salford Water Company was emerging on the future aims of a more ambitious water undertaking. In 1844 J.F. Bateman was invited by the Manchester Corporation to become their Consulting Engineer, tasked with finding a new water supply advising them on obtaining a purer and more abundant supply of clean and wholesome water for the city and surrounding area. J.F.B. was about to embark on the most challenging and daunting period of his life; he began designing the Longdendale Valley Reservoirs.

Bateman, at 36 years of age, was proving to be an astute businessman as well as a talented engineer, as can be seen from his report to the Manchester Corporation regarding his scheme to extract water from the River Etherow. In a letter dated 30 July 1846, Bateman reported: 'Before bringing this project formally before the Corporation, I communicated with the solicitors of several of the more influential mill owners who had opposed the Water Company in their application to Parliament in 1845, with a view of ascertaining whether a scheme would be likely to meet with their approval. I was of the opinion that they were far too enlightened, and too much alive to their own interests, to stand long in the way of a scheme which could be proved to be one of mutual benefit to them.' And he was proved to be right.

Due to Manchester's ever-expanding cotton industry, engineering, and manufacturing of machinery for the textile industry, this was an ever-growing town with a population which grew from 32,200 in 1801 to 1,000,000 by 1850. Lady Manchester came of age when she was granted her Municipal Charter in 1838. Nine years later, in 1847, the 'city fathers' boasted of becoming a city, by celebrating the creation and opening of their public parks, but at last they were also turning their attention to the vexed question of the city's unsanitary housing conditions, lacking in basic health provisions. The Manchester and Salford Water Company was also pressing ahead to extend its water mains into the newly acquired suburb districts and townships which by now had been amalgamated under the new charter. In 1851 an Act of Parliament authorised the Corporation to introduce a halfpenny rate to create museums and public libraries, and shortly later, free hospitals for the treatment of the poor, and most importantly the introduction of underground sewers, all improving the living conditions of its people. None of these improvements in health and environmental issues would have been possible without that important element, H_20. Water was vital for Manchester's ambition of becoming a progressive city.

After a lapse of 40 years, from way back in 1808 when the first call went out from the people of Manchester to control their own water supply, the dream was about to be realised. On 9 July 1847 the Manchester Corporation Water Act came into force, empowering the Manchester Corporation to purchase the Manchester and Salford Waterworks Company. By January 1848, the Corporation had applied to the Commissioners for loans of £20,000, beginning in April. The loan was granted on 10 June 1848, thus enabling the construction of the new Longdendale reservoirs to commence, which J.F. Bateman had pushed for so long to achieve. Commencing with the Woodhead Reservoir and the Mottram Tunnel in 1848, 1,000 labourers, with their pickaxes and shovels, grafted on for almost thirty years, ably supported by steam-powered machinery to complete these historic works.

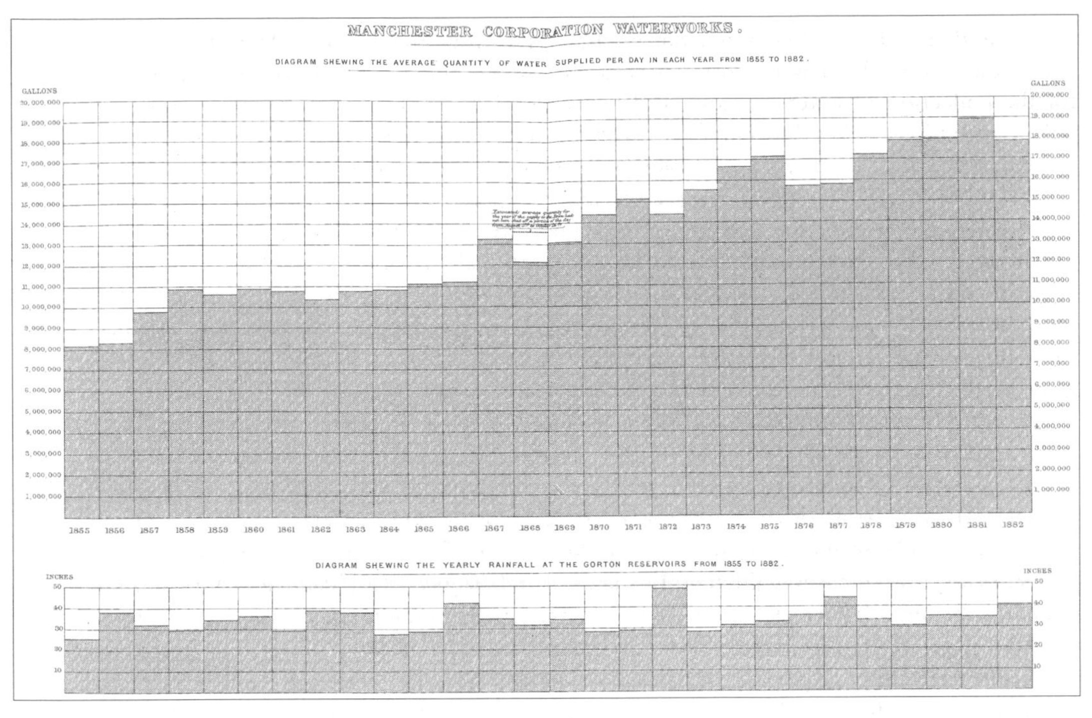

Diagram simultaneously showing the average quantity of water supplied to Manchester per year, commencing in 1855, with 8.2 million gallons per day, rising to almost 19 million gallons in 1882, and the annual rainfall at the Gorton reservoirs, over the same period. Note that the average rainfall at Gorton was 35in per year, as opposed to the Longdendale rainfall of 52.5in. An interesting anomaly occurred in 1868, when the town water supply was shut for a portion of the day, from 3 August to 26 October.

At last, in 1855, water began flowing towards Manchester via the Mottram Tunnel and the city was endowed with its first reliable water supply, which has never run dry. These historic works were completed in 1877 and the City of Manchester had successfully fulfilled the largest and most ambitious public health scheme ever attempted in Europe.

By an Act of Parliament in 1924 the Corporation went on to construct the major supplies of Thirlmere and Haweswater in the Lake District, to supply homes across Manchester and Lancashire, so proving itself once more as one of the most progressive and dynamic Corporation Water Works in the UK, and successfully enduring trial and tribulation for over 125 years. Today, the chain of Victorian reservoirs in the Longdendale Valley, supported by service storage reservoirs at Godley, Denton, and the largest at Audenshaw which were constructed between 1844 and 1875, still provide more than 1.5 million people with a reliable yield of 102 megalitres (Ml), or 22.5 million gallons per day of pure wholesome water, serving people in East Manchester, Stockport, Glossop and Tameside.

Unfortunately there were other corporations and privately owned waterworks within the water industry who were far less efficient, prompting further changes. One of the aims of the reorganisation was to identify water requirements over entire regions and to define a water network capable of distributing water supplies throughout England and Wales, and encouraging water authorities to consider at all times making greater use of valuable water resources to ensure, as Bateman once put it, 'That prime necessity of life – WATER!'

The Water Act 1973 set up 10 publicly owned authorities who had responsibility for managing the provision of both drinking water supplies and also for managing sewerage, treatment and environmental issues. This was in addition to seventeen water companies dealing with clean water only. Thus in 1974, the North West Water Authority was created to amalgamate more than 250 municipal and privately owned water companies throughout the north west of England.

The Act of 1989 dismissed public ownership and led to the privatisation of the water authorities, giving rise to ten water and sewerage companies, and the National Rivers Authority, which became part of the Environment Agency, responsible for such things as water resources, pollution control, flood defence, and fisheries.

The Water Industry Act 1991 included several important amendments, including removing the companies' ability to disconnect household customers for non-payment of charges. In July 1995 North West Water Ltd placed a bid to acquire the regional electricity company, Norweb, and they eventually succeeded in embracing both the water and electricity companies in 2001. Although the water and electricity businesses remained separate working companies, the names North West Water and Norweb were dropped in the formation of the new powerful company, United Utilities.

Even today, water authorities are still struggling to get it right. Pollution incidents, with the erratic discharge of raw sewage, are still making headlines and many incidents are caused by the water industry itself. Complaints of dead fish in rivers still cause problems in some areas. Regularly we have reports either of areas plagued by drought with hosepipe bans, or residents distressed by the constant fear of their homes being flooded. It is hard to believe that some parts of England have less water per head, per household, than say Spain or Portugal. One long hot summer left many reservoirs with a supply of less than fifty per cent of storage water with which to face the year ahead and we face the prospect of such summers becoming the norm. A prediction that there will be a shortage of water sets the alarm bells ringing and it is a challenge which every household has a responsibility to meet – to save this precious commodity which many people take for granted. The Water companies are aware of these problems and are constantly striving to remedy faults which they know exist, and who knows when or why the next reorganisation will take place - but eventually, it will.

seven

Reservoir Safety

Reservoir Safety Legislation

On 2nd November 1925, a disaster struck the village of Dolgarrog in North Wales, involving two nearby reservoirs. Due to a high rainfall intensity, the embankment of the smaller upstream Eigiau Reservoir was breached, causing, in a short time, water to flood downstream to the Coety Reservoir which filled to overflowing and, under the weight of millions of gallons of water, the Coety Reservoir dam collapsed. The force of the flooding water rolled boulders as though they were ping-pong balls and hurled them, together with trees and debris, down on the peaceful village of Dolgarrog, swamping the immediate area. This calamity resulted in the sad deaths of sixteen people, and there was a public outcry demanding more stringent safety reservoir control. An investigation on British dam failures concluded that during the period between 1831–1930, there were gross engineering deficiencies and failures due to over-topping, especially in the capacity of the spillways, overflows and reservoir floodwater channels.

The first attempts to legislate for the safety of reservoirs appears to have been the Waterworks Clause Act 1863, which contained some limited provisions, but it was the Dolgarrog disaster which prompted Parliament to implement the Reservoirs (Safety Provisions) Act of 1930. The Act, which was updated by the UK Reservoirs Act of 1975, further enforced laws on the safety of reservoirs. Under this Act every reservoir with a capacity of 25,000cu. m of water or more has to be inspected at least every 10 years, or more frequently depending on other prevailing conditions such as the age of the reservoir. The Act clearly makes reservoir owners legally responsible for the safety of their reservoirs. Reservoir inspections must only be carried out by experienced, qualified civil engineers, who are appointed to a special 'panel'. Panel engineers are experts on reservoir construction with knowledge of reservoir safety matters, and they are designated to such panels on the recommendation of the Institute of Civil Engineers and officially appointed by the Secretary of State. A panel appointment lasts for five years and not ten years as was the case under the 1930 Act. The panel engineer makes visual inspections on both the dam and its surrounding territory, searching for any leakage or damp area on the earth embankments; reed grass can be one indication of this. The inspection engineer looks for cracks, bulges or hollows on the reservoir crests and embankments. They are not only responsible for the necessary design and supervision of the work required, but they must also inspect and verify that such necessary alterations and improvements have been successfully carried out by the responsible reservoir proprietors. Inspecting engineers' investigations are based on the Probable Maximum Flood (PMF) that may be expected from the most severe combinations of critical meteorologic and hydraulic conditions that are reasonably possible in the area of the particular reservoir under scrutiny. Panel engineers have many responsibilities and only the cream of the profession, with confidence in their own ability to take on such onerous work, are suitable.

Environmental Considerations

With the Longdendale Valley being within the boundaries of the Peak District National Park, many factors have to be taken into consideration before reservoir safety reconstruction work can be put into operation, apart from the call of vital emergency work.

Actual work schedules cannot even be contemplated without prior consultation with local people and many other interested parties, and it is essential therefore to seek their co-operation by requesting opinions and written comments. The Peak District National Park, the Environmental Agencies, the High Peak District Council, local Parish, District, Borough and Metropolitan Councils, including special interest groups, and farmers, all have to be considered.

The Peak District National Park, with its many activities and environmental developments within its boundaries, forms an essential component of negotiations with the water company which include planning permission, heights of structures, colour of materials and the diversion of footpaths, along with other important considerations during construction work, such as agreeing alternative routes for roads crossing over embankment crests.

A similar pattern applies to farmers in order that they may continue to have access and egress to their farm and farmland, and surrogate roads must be made available to minimise their loss of time. If heavy plant is being used within hearing distance of houses, or even an isolated cottage or farmhouse, noise levels must be reduced to a minimum.

When a reservoir has overhead power or telephone cables crossing over and situated alongside the embankment road this often causes a blot on the landscape, and consideration should be given to finding an alternative arrangement. This can be done by either seeking a different route away from the embankment crest, or by burying the offending line below ground level. If an overhead crane has to be brought on site, overhead cables can be a hindrance and a danger to the crane operator, so removal of overhead power lines can be beneficial for future embankment maintenance work.

If there are fish in a reservoir, and the reservoir level is being drawn down to facilitate reservoir construction, then a fish rescue plan must be put into operation. This is accomplished by a qualified fishing bailiff first netting the fish, checking them to ensure they are free from disease, before transferring them into suitable oxygen-supplied tanks. The fish may then be transported to a new location and either directly released downstream into the river, or taken to waters operated by an angling club to augment their fish stocks.

The Environmental Agency can be affected by the lowering of reservoirs, for if a reservoir is lowered excessively and silt is allowed to be dragged along by the flow of water entering the River Etherow, this can cause the death of hundreds of fish, overtaken by silt entering their gills and choking them, resulting in dead fish floating downstream which could contaminate the river.

Because the high surrounding upland moorland is of a deep peaty nature, the water becomes discoloured and acidic, for the Longdendale Reservoirs are noted for their heavy silt content from the iron and manganese caused by colloidal suspended clay being deposited after heavy rainfall. Therefore, whilst the reservoir levels are lowered to facilitate reconstruction work, advantage should be taken to remove the silt thus giving extra water storage. The silt is excavated from the reservoir and deposited and stockpiled and made available to be sold to contractors requiring infill on building sites or spoil for garden landscaping.

J.F. Bateman ensured that the Longdendale Reservoirs were magnificently constructed in hand-crafted masonry and over the years the water authority, whenever practically possible, has adhered to this principle. To ensure continuity, whenever unsightly reinforced concrete structures have to be built they are faced either with masonry or reconstituted concrete cladding to minimise their ugly appearance. Long may these reservoirs be a source of inspiration to engineers and a delight to visitors travelling from near or far.

Reservoir Safety In Motion

The chain of five reservoirs in the Longdendale Valley, connected by the River Etherow, is almost six miles long, the longest chain of reservoirs in the world back in the late-eighteenth century, yet they are still supplying a reliable yield of water, together with Arnfield Reservoir which is fed from tributaries of the River Etherow, to provide 22.5 million gallons of water per day. From 1887 regular reservoir safety inspections checks have taken place, and in 1966 former Manchester Corporation Waterworks appointed T&C Hawksley, Consulting Engineers, to investigate, report, and if necessary recommend safety work required under the Reservoirs Safety Provisions Act 1930, on all six reservoirs at Longdendale. Model hydraulic conditions were carried out on the Longdendale Reservoirs at Salford University under the auspices of the late Professor Wilson, Head of the Hydraulics Department. These investigations resulted in a considerable amount of reservoir safety improvement work being executed on the reservoirs. I briefly mentioned the forthcoming improvement safety works, as described more fully below, in the first edition of my book, page 55.

With the introduction of the Reservoir Safety Act 1975, a Statutory Report by Mr R.T. Gerrard, dated 12 June 1984, showed that all of the five reservoirs had insufficient freeboard to prevent the dams being over-topped during a Probable Maximum Flood. As the safety conditions could not be fulfilled, Binnie & Partners were commissioned by North West Water Authority to carry out feasibility studies on the five Longdendale reservoirs. Their report, submitted in December 1984, recommended that Woodhead Reservoir, being at the fountain head of the chain of reservoirs, should be adopted to provide sufficient flood storage during times of excessive floods, which would reduce the peak flows passing through the other four reservoirs.

In February 1985 Binnie & Partners were instructed to proceed with the next stage of the preliminary design of the general embankment and spillways, which included hydraulic model studies and testing of flood conditions. Three years later Babie Shaw & Morton were commissioned to provide more detailed designs and to supervise the intended safety improvement work at Woodhead based on the principles established by the earlier preliminary designs. Three other panel member experts were also commissioned to overview and report on the design, which demonstrates the huge amount of care and painstaking work involving a host of skilled consulting engineers to produce the correct solution and to ensure the safety of the reservoirs in order to prevent any possible future disasters. With an average rainfall of 52.2 in (1,333mm) over a catchment area of 19,000 acres (7,700 hectares) that's a lot of water to tame.

For an interesting account of the Longdendale Valley's worst flooding, which reached catastrophic proportions back in October of 1849 and in February 1852, please refer to pages 55–58.

Woodhead Reservoir

No doubt, if the great man J.F. La Trobe Bateman had been asked the question 'Was the Woodhead Reservoir your 'Achilles' Heel'?', he would have readily agreed, for it had taken him almost 40 years to obtain a watertight embankment. Then we have to remember that this ingenious engineer was the pioneer of earthen dams, a man who was designing and constructing, for the first time ever, reservoirs of gigantic proportions, larger than anything ever attempted by any water engineer in the whole world at that time. He was literally working in uncharted muddy waters of shifting sands and moving hillsides. Little wonder that in 1852 he called upon the services and advice of two other respected eminent Victorian engineers of the day, Mr Robert Stephenson and Mr I.K. Brunel.

Stephenson and Brunel visited the works and, after much discussion with J.F.B, they decided on a course of action. Shortly after their visit, J.F.B. tells us, 'various shafts were sunk and driftways driven, for the purpose of ascertaining accurately the depth and character of the moving mass, the nature of the material on which it had moved, and the quantity of water contained in the hillside'. From the results obtained and what happened next, Bateman explains:

The watercourse intended to be constructed across the slips, except that for the conveyance of floodwaters, were abandoned; the pure water of the streams and springs from the higher parts of the valley was conveyed under the slips by cast iron pipes, and a large supply of pure spring - water drawn from the base of the slipping ground by the various driftways, and conveyed direct to Manchester by the watercourse commencing below the Rhodeswood Reservoir.

Unfortunately this was not the complete answer, for much more work was to follow, including reconstructing the first embankment with a second embankment, which commenced in 1862. The Woodhead Embankment was finally sealed and made water-tight in 1877 (see page 70 for more details).

Referring to his thirty years of experience within the Woodhead Reservoir, J.F. Bateman admitted, as only a great man can: 'Notwithstanding all the experiences I have had, and my willingness to learn by failures as well as success, I am far from having any decided view as to the best means of drawing water from a great reservoir. Each case must be considered with reference to its peculiar circumstances, and no informal or universal mode can be recommended or adopted.' So spoke this most celebrated of all reservoir designers, further revealing, the difficult task panel one engineers have to face and the careful decisions they have to make, even today with far more specific and scientifically recorded evidence to fall back on.

As Woodhead Reservoir was the first and highest in the chain of reservoirs in the valley, the panel engineers decided major work was required, in order to considerably increase the flood water storage in Woodhead, and thus reduce peak flows on the other four downstream reservoirs. This was contrary to increasing the water storage in Woodhead Reservoir, as. the overflow level of the reservoir would remain the same. To do this, the level of the embankment crest was raised by an enormous 6.7m, which meant replacing the original road across the dam at a higher level. Thus the B6105 road which crossed the original dam was diverted and re routed to pass over the crest of the new raised embankment, as shown on the cross-sectional drawing below.

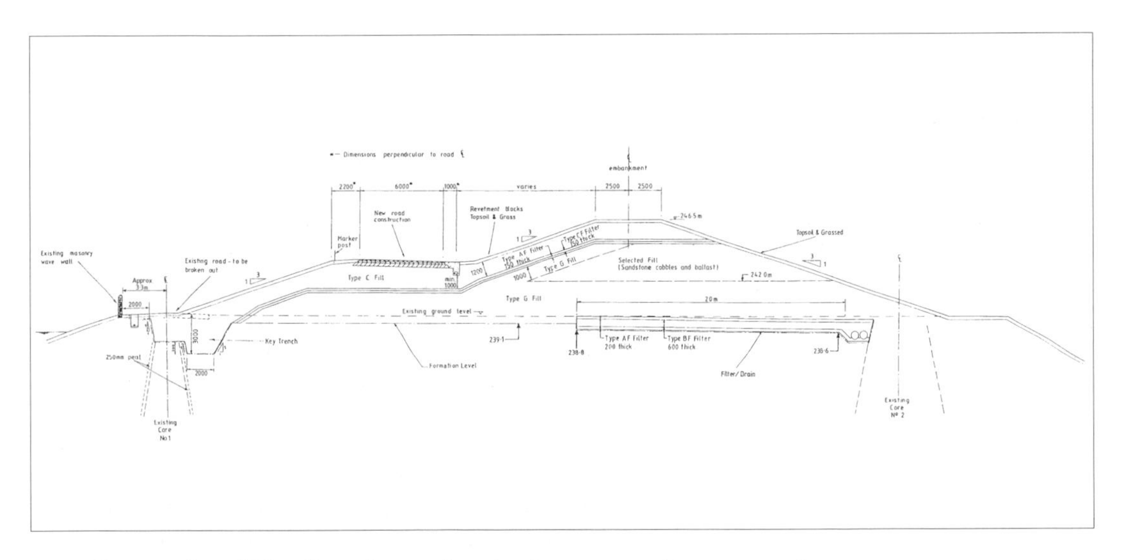

Cross-section of Woodhead Reservoir embankment as newly constructed.

One of the important tasks was to lay an impervious clay membrane on the upstream face of the raised section to provide continuity from the original second embankment improvement work which had been completed by Bateman in 1877. Any seepage occurring within the embankment during any future severe flood conditions would be collected in a new longitudinal drainage system provided at the base of the new embankment. The upstream slope was protected by precast concrete revetment matting whilst the downstream slope of the existing embankment was structurally supported and the toe drainage improved. The reservoir overflow sill was not altered but the overall length of the sill was reduced and a "throttle" incorporated in a new concrete box culvert section of the spillway passing through the raised embankment. The downstream spillway chute was replaced by a new channel which discharges into the Etherow Pool below. An old control valve was replaced by a 1,400mm diameter guard valve together with other associated pipework. The contract for this work was let out in 1989, to Kennedy Construction, and the works completed in 1992, at a total cost of £3,000,000.

This is in stark contrast to the cost, between 1848 and 1877, of constructing the entire works of five reservoirs in the Longdendale Valley, including Arnfield and Hollingworth reservoirs, the Aqueducts and the Mottram Tunnel – the total cost being £3,147,893!

Torside Reservoir

Torside is the second reservoir downstream from the fountainhead and approximately 40m lower than Woodhead Reservoir. It is the single largest reservoir in the Longdendale Valley, being 2.25 km long and 26m (84 feet) deep, capable of holding in excess of 6,700 megalitres, (1.474 million gallons), and covering an area of 160 acres.

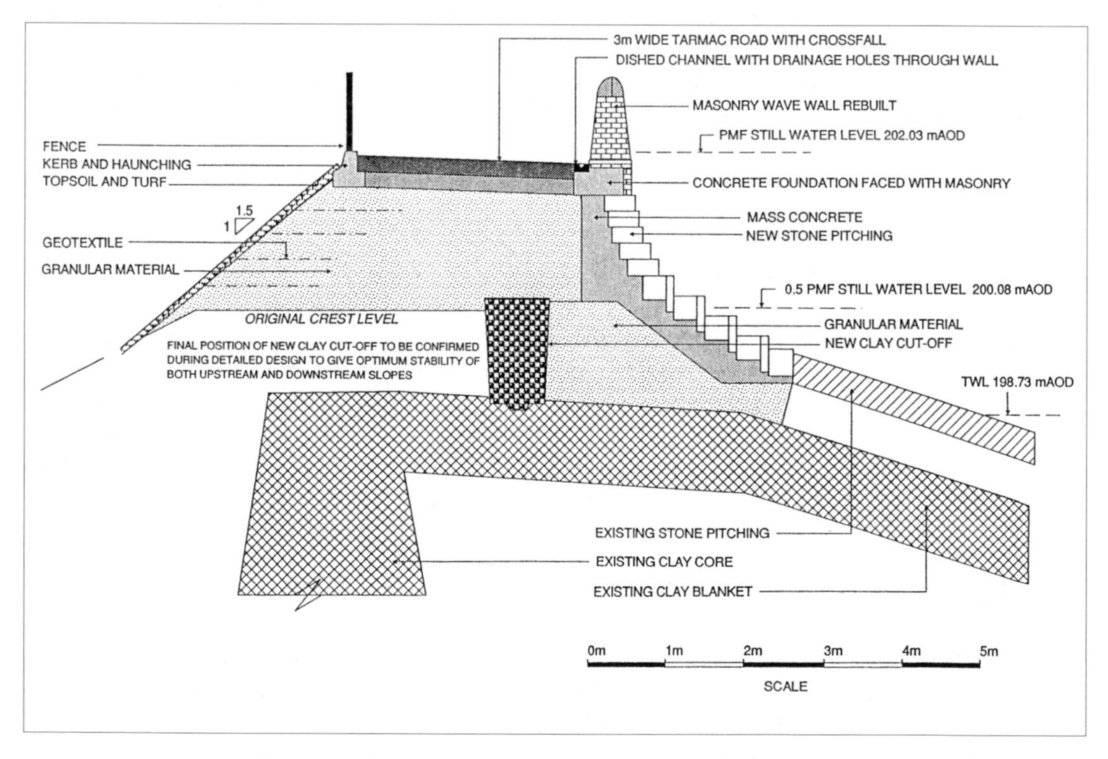

Torside Embankment crest remedial work.

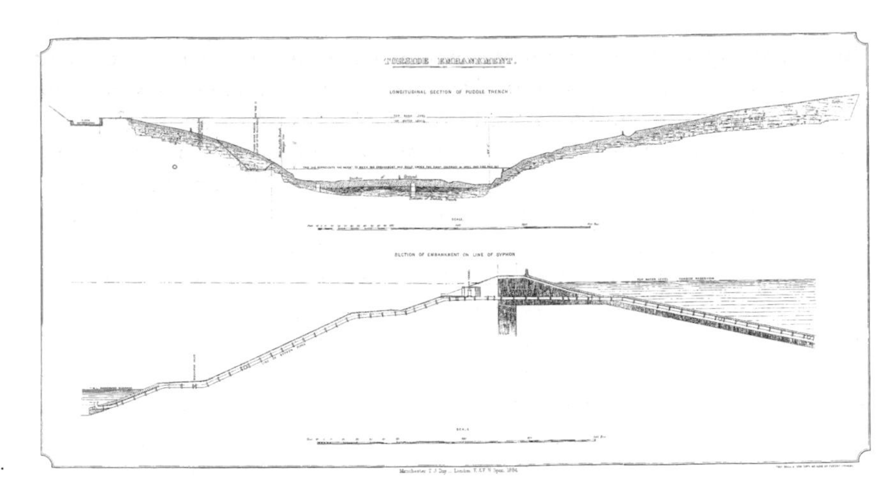

Torside embankment longitudinal section, 1864.

To some extent the proposed work of Torside Reservoir depended on the modifications carried out at Woodhead Reservoir as described above. Before final decisions could be made, model testing assimilating flood conditions were undertaken. Mott MacDonald UK Limited was commissioned to organise and supervise the model testing of the spillways both at Torside and Rhodeswood, the model testing being carried out by The University of Manchester Institute of Science and Technology (UMIST) in November 1990. To improve safety on Torside Reservoir, the second in the chain of five reservoirs, it was found that more work was required than originally intended, resulting in the following construction work being carried out, as stated in Appendix 3, of the Project Definition:

(a) Demolish the existing wave wall and reconstruct a new wall on top of the raised embankment, with a minimum level of 4.04m above the overflow sill level to provide an adequate wave barrier.

(b) To raise the clay core of the embankment to 1.34m above the overflow sill level, including raising the stone pitching.

(c) Raise the road level to a minimum of 3.29m above the overflow level.

These improvements would necessitate the construction of a new tarmacadam road across the reservoir embankment. Please refer to cross-sectional drawing of the embankment crest opposite. The work included raising the flood water course road bridge parapets to 1.2m above the new road level, the modification of valves in the valve shaft, reconditioning of the 'Dungeon Valve', replacement of the badly corroded ladders, and other minor ancillary works. The work commenced in 1993 and was completed in 1994, by Morrison Construction, at a total cost of £1,617,000.

Rhodeswood Reservoir

Woodhead, Torside, and Rhodeswood are all reservoirs storing water for supply purposes. It is Rhodeswood Reservoir, number three downstream from the fountain head, from whence the actual water is extracted and fed into supply via the Mottram Tunnel and Longdendale Aqueduct. Following consultants' reports and results from hydraulic model testing on the Rhodeswood Reservoir, the panel engineers concluded the following work was required:

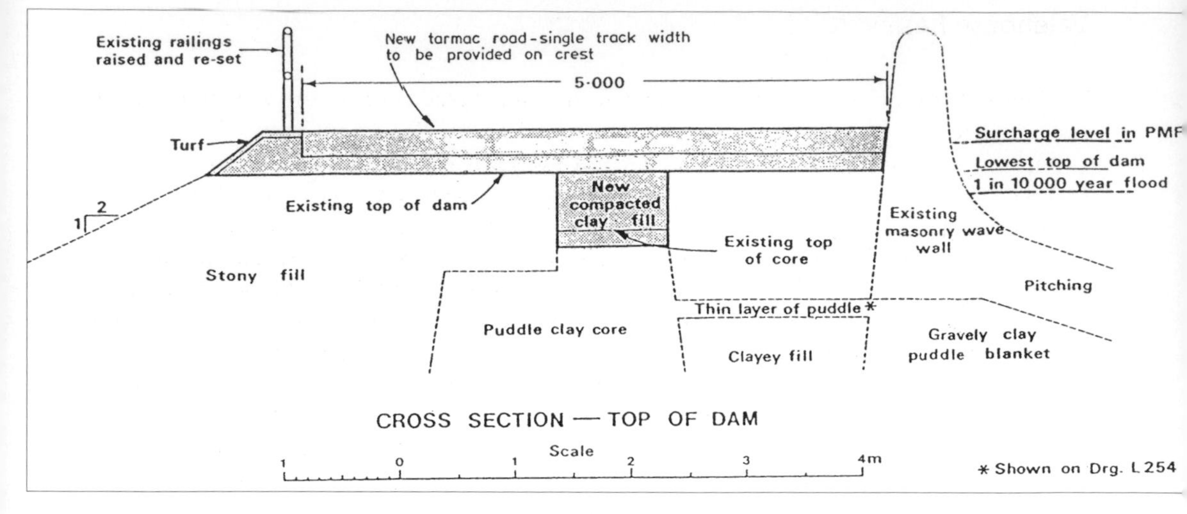

Cross-section of newly constructed Rhodeswood embankment (dam).

It was found that the spillways were capable of passing the Probable Maximum Flood, without over-topping the embankment (dam), but consideration was required regarding the North spillway channel, where J.F. Bateman had encountered earth movement problems during the construction of the Rhodeswood Reservoir. Damage to this channel could result in the entire discharge from the North weir overflowing into Valehouse and Bottoms Reservoirs, thus causing possible dam failures, and putting at risk the communities of Tintwistle, Hadfield, and parts of Glossop. It was therefore decided to model test the Southern overflow sill and overflow tunnel which would lessen the overloading of the North spillway, which would also require model testing in order to conclude how best to improve the overall discharge conditions. After the model testing results to both Rhodeswood and Torside were analysed, it was found that the original concept of safety work was no longer necessary, resulting in less construction work being required.

It was therefore decided to press ahead with reservoir safety as follows:

(a) To raise the embankment level by a minimum of 40mm over the existing road, to form a single track tarmacadam access road.

(b) To raise slightly the existing masonry wave wall to a minimum height of 1.2m above the new road level.

(c) Minor modifications of the South Spillway Tunnel portal by forming a concrete fairing block inside the existing headwall and raising the existing wing walls 0.5m above the maximum flood level. (Please refer to the drawing below showing the modifications to the tunnel entrance.)

(d) To regrade the access road with gabion protection to the embankment side, adjacent to the North spillway, to prevent erosion due to over topping of the spillway walls.

The main contractor for the above work was Johnson Construction; work commenced in 1994 and was completed in 1995 at a total cost of £638,000.

Valehouse Reservoir

Valehouse Reservoir is the penultimate or fourth in the cascade of five reservoirs in the valley and is the first of the two compensation reservoirs, Bottoms Reservoir being the other one. Compensation water (please refer to pages 18-20) was first recognised by the insistence of the mill owners to compensate for loss of their water power, due to the river water being dammed up, and so stopping a supply of water to their mills during reservoir construction. (Vale House Mill was purchased by Manchester Corporation in 1864. By 1868, few villagers remained in the hamlet of Vale House. In 1869, Vale House was drowned out.) As Valehouse and Bottoms Reservoirs draw off levels are too low for the supply of drinking water to Manchester by gravity, both these reservoirs were designed exclusively for the supply of compensation water into the River Etherow. Today, ten million gallons (45 million litres) of water per day is still released into the river to sustain river flow and help eradicate pollution problems. As the difference between Valehouse and Bottoms reservoir top water levels is only 3.04m, a substantial proportion of the Valehouse embankment is normally submerged by the accumulating overflow water of Bottoms Reservoir. Valehouse embankment is of earthen construction with a central clay core similar to all the reservoirs in the valley chain. Between 1984 and 1986 studies were carried out to consider solutions to attain the required degree of flood protection at each of the two reservoirs. As hydraulic model testing had already been carried out to achieve flood protection on Woodhead, Torside and Rhodeswood Reservoirs, and using the in-flow hydrograph and solutions found on those reservoirs, together with other important data, such as the Valehouse bye channel being blocked by falling trees, the outcome of these exhaustive preliminary flood studies on Valehouse Reservoir resulted in the following safety work being implemented:

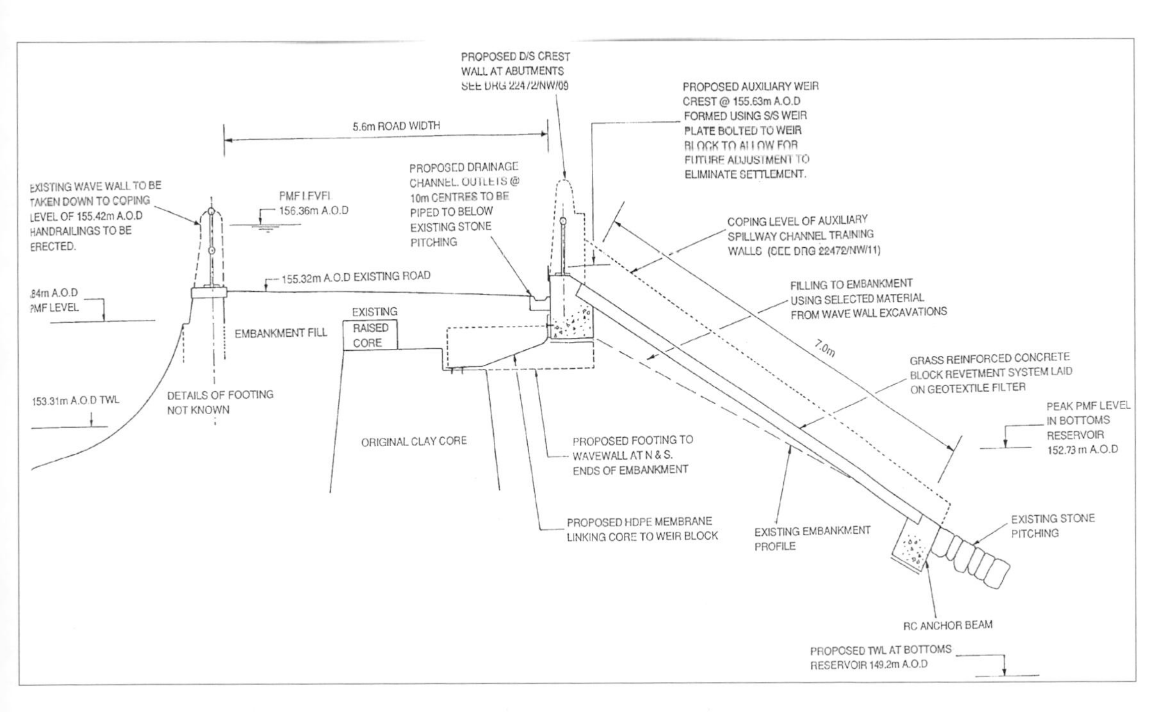

Cross-section of newly constructed Valehouse embankment (dam).

(1) Removal of the existing spillway bridge and replace with a reinforced concrete bridge deck with a soffit (underside of beam or arch) above the predicted PMF level. The bridge parapets are to be clad in masonry at a higher level.

(2) Raise the reservoir retention level by 3.81m and the embankment crest by 1.8m.

(3) Removal of the existing reservoir side wave wall, to existing crest level and erection of hand railing on the wall footings along the full length of the embankment and provide a wave wall at each end of the ancillary overflow on the downstream side

(4) Construction of an 80 metre wide auxiliary spillway over the down stream edge of the embankment face consisting of :

(a) A grass reinforced concrete block on the downstream edge of the embankment with a waterproof membrane linking the clay core to the weir block.

(b) Hand railing along the weir block.

(c) Protection of the downstream embankment face with a system of cable tied stayed reinforced concrete blocks.

(d) A toe beam cast against the upstream edge of the existing stone pitching.

(5) The work also included fitting 2 new 900mm butterfly valves down stream of the existing service valves, the motorisation of the new and existing valves, the descaling of draw off pipes and replacement of corroded flange bolts and repainting etc. and the crest road completely re surfaced on completion of the works.

(6) Re-routing of the 11 kV Norweb overhead power line into a duct laid along the embankment crest.

Bottoms Reservoir

Bottoms is the last in the chain of the five reservoirs, and the second of the compensation reservoirs, from whence is discharged the statutory 10 million gallons of compensation water per day required to continue the flow of the River Etherow. From information obtained during the model testing it was decided to include the following safety remedial work which had been started on site in September 1998:

(a) To raise the clay core and crest 2.5m, together with the wave wall to cope with the design flood pattern.

(b) To construct a dry-metalled track across the embankment (dam) crest.

(c) To replace the arch of the bridge, that crosses the overt low/bywash channel, with one that will give greater clearance beneath the bridge for the flow of water during flood conditions and to raise sections of the channel walls for the same reason. This work would also necessitate repositioning of the 150mm diameter main that crosses over and alongside the bridge.

(d) Re-pointing of the floor stonework of the Tumbling Bay and overflow byewash channel.

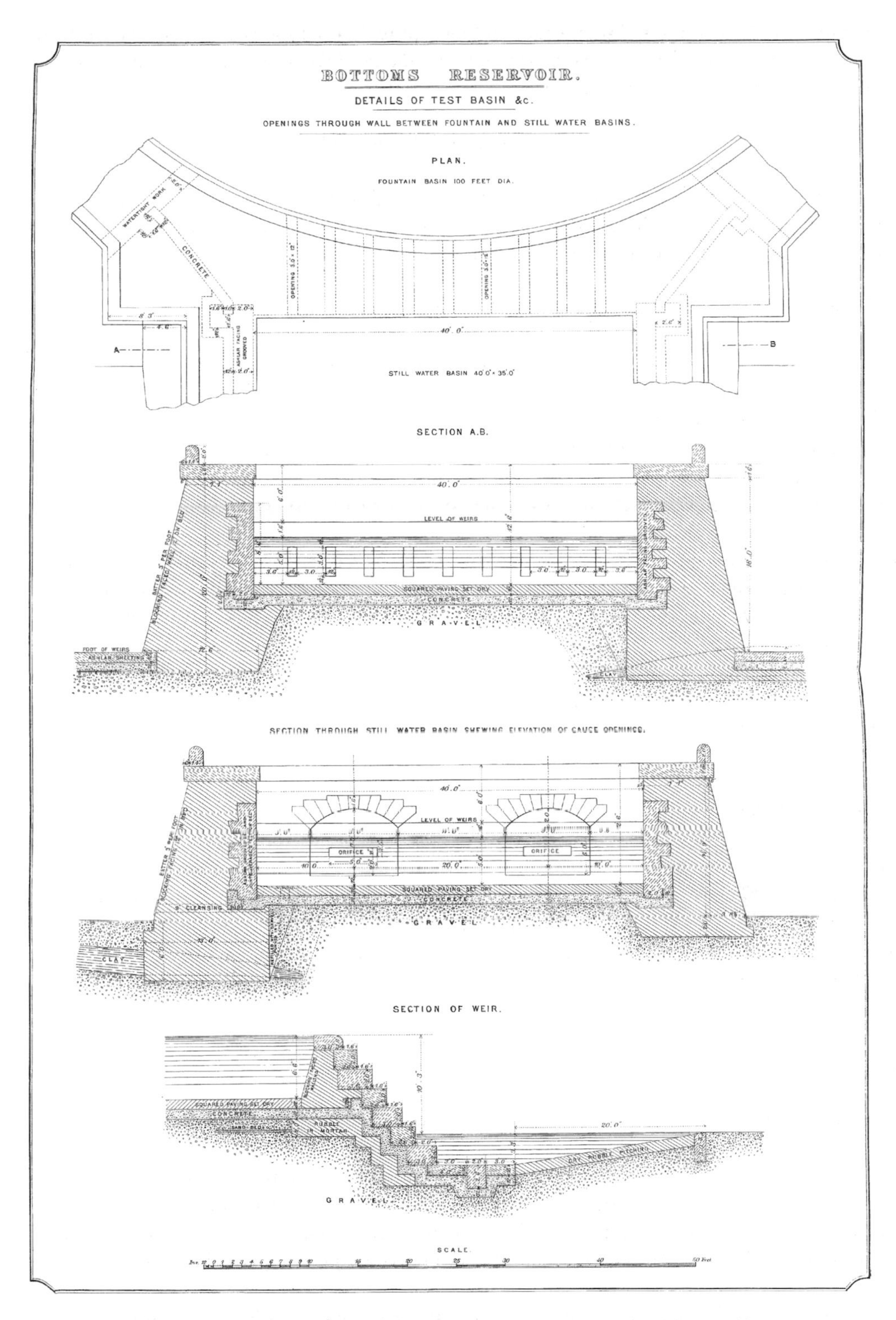

Bottoms test gauging basin, 1871 (see pictures on pages 85, 86, 89, 90).

REVERSING TUMBLER IN DISCHARGE TROUGHS.

FIG: I. ORDINARY OPEN POSITION.

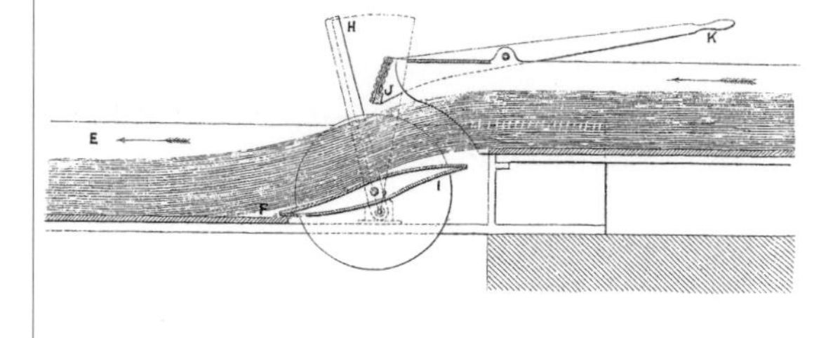

FIG: 2. TUMBLER REVERSED
DISCHARGING INTO TEST BASIN.

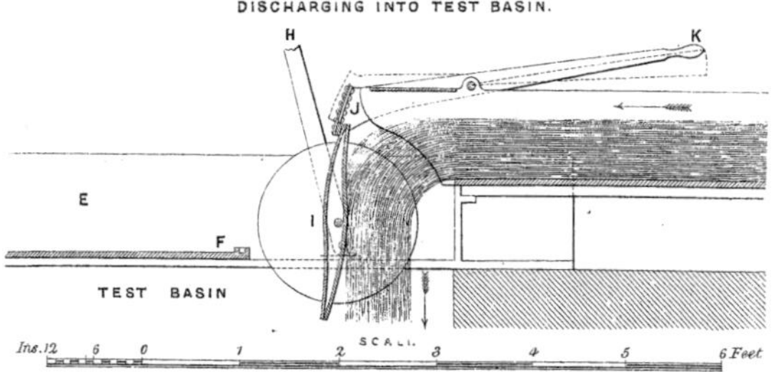

EXPLANATION.

In the bottom of the trough E, Fig. I., is placed a tumbler I in a horizontal position, turning on an axis in the centre, and this tumbler ordinarily forms the floor of the trough and the water passes over it; but on drawing back the hand lever H into the position shown by the dotted line, so that the extremity of the tumbler just clears the edge F of the trough, the tumbler is instantaneously reversed by the stream of water and turned vertically across the trough, where it is caught by the stop J, as shown in Fig. 2. In this position the water is discharged through the opening in the bottom of the trough into the test basin below, and at the same time the tumbler opposes an effectual barrier to its passing along the trough beyond the opening. The previous level of the water in the basin being noted, together with the time at which the stream is turned into it, the tumbler is again replaced at the end of a given interval in its original position, shown in Fig. I., by raising the stop J by the handle K so as to release the tumbler; the discharge of the water into the test basin is thus instantly arrested, and the water allowed to pass along the trough E, as before, into the river below. The height to which the basin has been filled during the time noted is then ascertained, and the quantity discharged is thereby accurately determined.

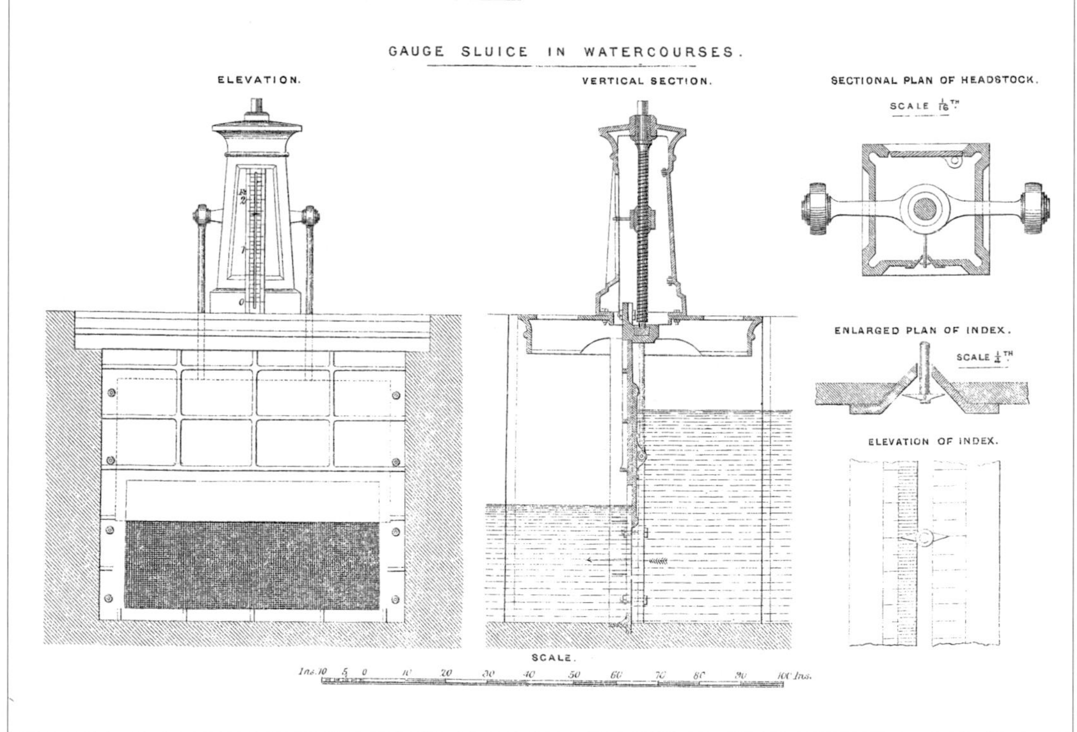

Drawing and explanation of discharging water into the test basin.

(e) Cleaning out the accumulated silt and sand from the inner and outer pools of tailbay and desilting the top pool of the bywash cascade.

(f) Other work included installation of an electrically operated Butterfly valve to the South pipe in the discharge tunnel, the installation of lighting and ventilation system in the upstream tunnel, cleaning and painting where necessary and repairs to all damaged stonework and any other faulty mechanism.

The remedial work for both Vale House and Bottoms Reservoir was carried out during 1989–1999 at a total cost of £1,500,000. The work was contracted to Pierse Contracting.

Arnfield Reservoir

Arnfield impounding reservoir, the smallest of the surviving six Longdendale reservoirs, with a holding capacity of 950 megalitres (209 million gallons), is not in the main valley floor, but is situated near Tintwistle, alongside the A628 road, and impounds water from the surrounding area mainly via the Arnfield Brook and Ogden Brook. The reservoir impounds water behind an earthen embankment 17m high comprising five embankments of 953m in length. A masonry overflow weir, situated in

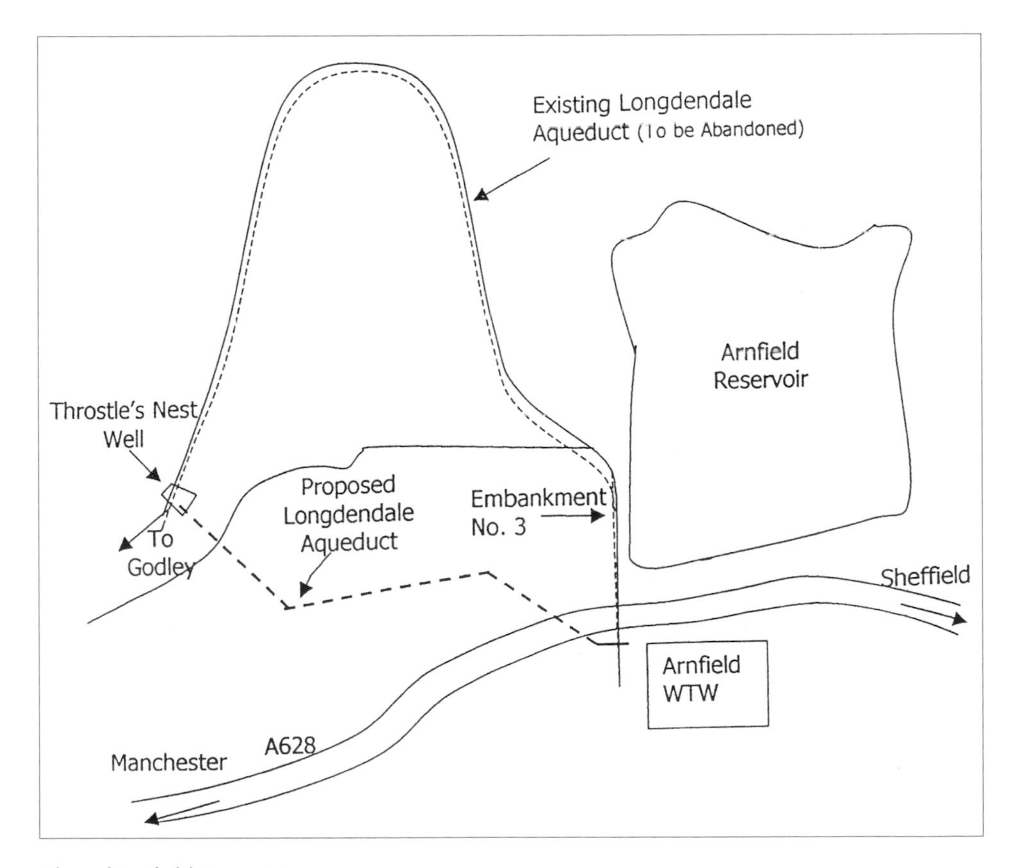

Plan of Arnfield Reservoir.

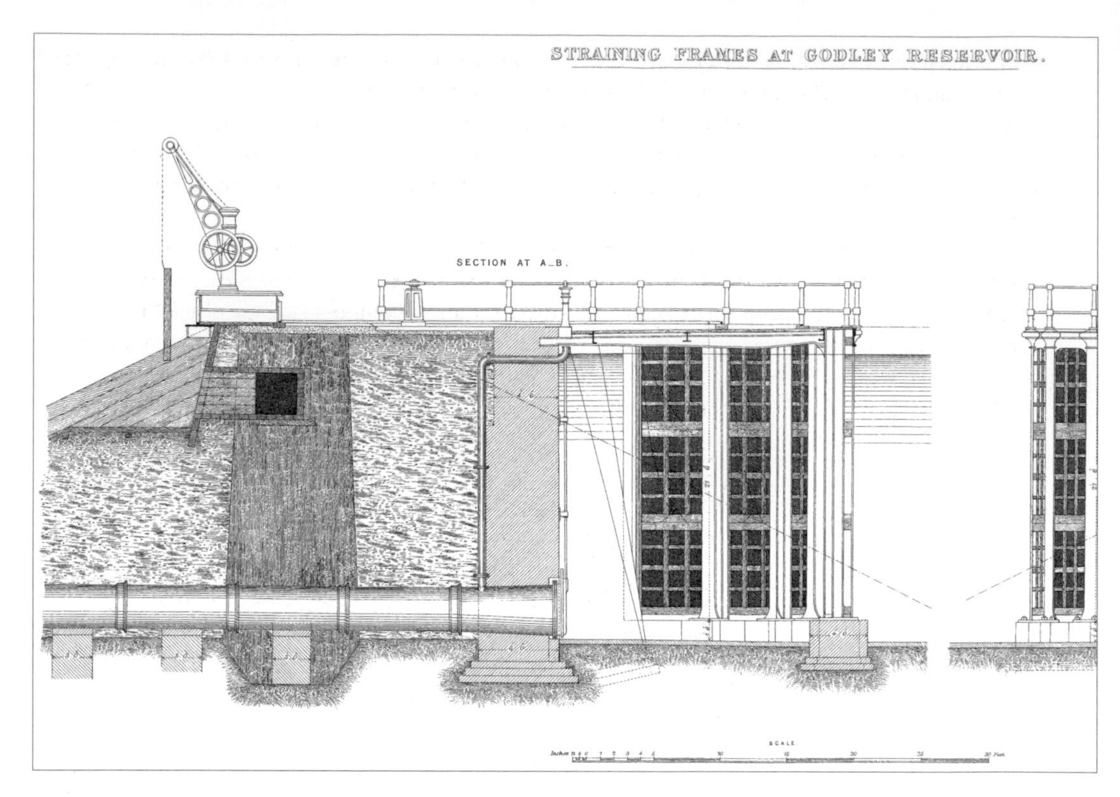

Cross-section of oak-framed, wire-gauge, straining frames. The frames were so heavy that they required a hand-operated derrick to lower them into position, and for lifting the frames out, prior to wire brushing and cleaning before being re-used.

the right hand abutment of the embankment, protects the dam by over topping water flowing into an overflow channel. In consequence of an embankment stability study, including a natural-earth-vibration risk factor analysis which indicated an unacceptable factor of safety against an embankment failure, it was therefore decided to eliminate the risks of the embankment being breached by drawing down the normal top water level, in consequence, all water flowing into the reservoir was diverted. The work was in two phases working simultaneously with each other:

Phase 1. To abandon a section of the existing trapezoidal open channel Longdendale Aqueduct, and to replace the section with 150m of 1,200mm diameter pipes to convey treated water from the Arnfield Treatment Plant flow dividing chamber across to Throstle's Nest, hence downstream to Godley Treatment Plant, as shown in the diagram opposite.

Other pipework included laying 150m of 1,200 mm diameter pipes from the WTW North overflow to the dividing chamber within the Arnfield WTW.

Phase 2. As Embankment No.3 has a history of instability with evidence of shallow surface slips, evidenced in the past when previous re medial work was necessary, it was decided that more work was essential in order to stabilise the earth embankments of the reservoir, this would also include stabilisation work on Embankment No.2. This work would provide the embankments with an acceptable factor of safety against future failure and allow the reservoir to safely impound water as it has for almost 150 years.

Contracted by Galiford Costain Joint Venture at an estimated cost of £1,500,000 and at the time of writing, January, 2004, the remedial works were still in progress.

Until the early 1960s, Longdendale raw water treatment consisted mainly of straining the water through wire gauge screens, with the addition of allowing the water to settle out in settling ponds, then being passed through a chlorinating unit to kill off bacteria, before being fed into the distribution system.

With the building and commissioning of Arnfield and Godley treatment plants, a far more sophisticated system is in operation. Basically, at Arnfield Treatment Plant, lime, ferric sulphate and polyelectrolite are added in concrete formed mixing chambers to a produce 'floc' which binds together the water impurities. The extracted impurities then sink and are removed in sedimentation tanks. Sludge is a by-product of the treatment works process and this is piped over to the Arnfield Sludge Treatment for disposal. The treated water continues its flow, via gravity,

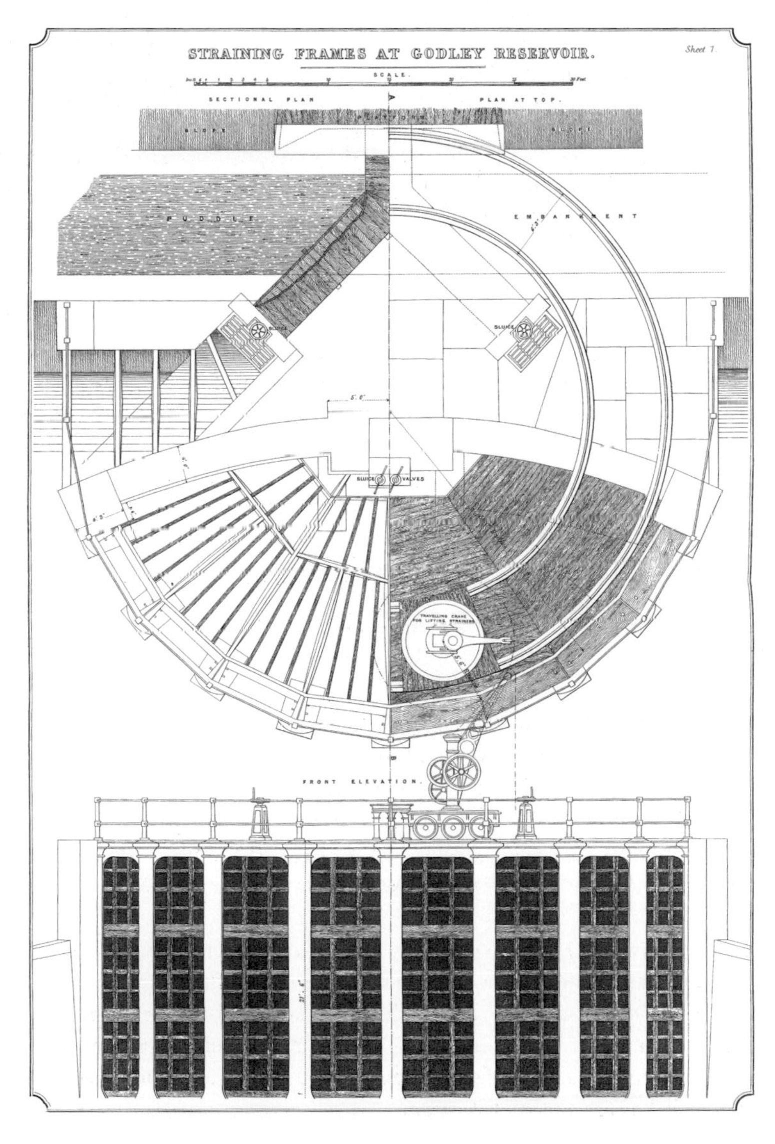

Diagrammatic plan showing Arnfield Reservoir.

through the five-and-a-half mile (9 km) long Mottram Tunnel to the Godley Treatment Plan, for final water treatment. Lime is added to remove the manganese from the water before being filtered and disinfected again with chlorine to kill bacteria and lurking germs before reaching domestic taps. The pure and wholesome water finally passes into covered service reservoirs before being fed into the distribution network and piped into homes.

Hollingworth Reservoir

Hollingworth Reservoir was the adjoining upstream reservoir to Arnfield Reservoir. It possessed its own Victorian stone-built fish hatchery, together with fish tanks and 3 fish cages anchored out in the middle of the reservoir for breeding brown and rainbow trout. MCWW employed its own full-time fishing Bailiff to supervise fish breeding and caring for the fish, and healthy 8 inch plus trout were used to stock the Bottoms, Valehouse and other reservoirs. Hollingworth Reservoir was drained off, filled in, and levelled off in October 1990 to return to its natural state. It is now part of the Swallows Wood nature reserve, but there are now plans in hand to possibly build a new motorway bypass through the land which was once a proud and picturesque reservoir.

DUTIES OF RESERVOIR KEEPERS.

WOODHEAD RESERVOIR.

AREA, 135 ACRES ; **CAPACITY,** 1,181,000,000 GALLONS ;
DEPTH, 71 FEET.

The Reservoir Keeper to commence his duties at 6-0 a.m.

To take reading of rain gauge, ascertain level of reservoir, nd adjust the valves in the valve shaft as may be required.

To gauge the spring water collected from the whole dis- :ict above Woodhead Embankment at the gauge in the pring Watercourse immediately below such embankment.

Then to gauge the Paper Mill Spring, make up the daily :port for the Town Hall, and take the same to the .eservoir Keeper at Torside. On returning, to walk along ıe Spring Watercourse to Crowden Brook, clean grids, and :camine work generally.

Breakfast at 8-30 a.m.

To go along the Derbyshire side of the valley to see the ındition of the springs, fences, &c., of the Corporation.

Dinner at 12-0 noon.

In the afternoon to walk along the watercourse from the servoir embankment up to Heyden Weir, and from Heyden 'eir to the Etherow Weir ; to examine the watercourse, the le of the reservoir, fences, residuum lodges, grids, &c., d return about 3-0 p.m.

To fill up the afternoon by attending to the weeding of ılks, repairing of road over reservoir embankment, cleaning valves, painting, and other sundry work necessary to keep : works at this reservoir in good order.

To see that all valves, sluices, and any machinery for working same, weirs, and other appliances are kept in good working order and condition ; to report immediately any-thing found defective on the works.

In the event of circumstances occurring requiring assistance, or a night watchman, application must be made without delay to the Reservoir Keeper at Bottoms.

In cases of emergency, or anything requiring special attention, immediate instructions must be obtained from the Town Hall ; or after official hours from ~~Mr. J. C. Eastham, The Thorns, Hadfield.~~ Mr. J. Hardy. Bottoms Lodge

On alternate Sundays a substitute will be provided to relieve the Reservoir Keeper from his duties, unless there be special circumstances as to floods which will require his attendance. At all other times he is expected to be on duty, unless he shall have obtained leave of absence from the Town Hall.

By order of the Waterworks Committee,

WM. HENRY TALBOT, Town Clerk.

Town Hall, Manchester,
January, 1897.

Examples of duties from reservoir keeper's duty book.

547
128

Manchester Corporation Water Works
Probable cost of Engineering Works

	original Estimate	Estimate June 1850	Estimated of actual Cost July 1851	Excess over Estimate of June 1850
Woodhead Reservoir	10.375	34.400	41.000	6.600
Watercourse fm. Woodhead to Arnfield	4.642	4.500	7.000	2.500
Crowden Reservoir	~~11.110~~	3.500	3.400 a	"
Arnfield & Hollingworth Reservoirs	26.031.10/	34.000	34.000	"
Arnfield Moor Reservoir	5.910	"	"	"
Drains on the Moors	2.970	2.000	3.000	1.000
Hollingworth Water Course Mottram Tunnel, & Tetlow Fold Watercourse	27.762	43.860	48.500	4.640
Godley Reservoir	7.150	8.150	10.100	1.950
Gauge Weir below Woodhead Reservoir	1.100	2.800	2.500 b	"
40 inch main pipe fm. Godley to Denton	43.589	31.000	34.000	3.000
Denton Service Reservoir	7.577.10/	11.770	13.900	2.130
[illegible] inch Main Pipe from Denton to Ardwick	37.828	28.000	30.000	2.000
Torside & Rhodes Wood Reservoir	52.525	58.034	63.500	5.466
Millowners' Gauge Basin	2.575	3.500	5.600	2.100

Copy of Bateman's original costing sheet showing estimates of engineering works to 1851.

Longdendale Hydro Scheme

One of the most interesting and satisfying innovations at Longdendale is the reintroduction of generating electricity, originally achieved back in 1877 at Bottoms Reservoir and which produced sufficient power to drive the works' electric railway train and supply power for Bottoms' offices and workshops. The power supply was terminated 28 years later in 1850. Longdendale celebrated the millennium of 2,000 with the installation of three hydro turbines, feeding a total of 240 kWh directly into the National Grid. The first unit was located at Torside Reservoir, from where a constant flow of water is discharged into Rhodeswood Reservoir to keep Rhodeswood Reservoir full. This turbine successfully produces 115 kilowatts per hour.

The second turbine was installed at the outlet from Rhodeswood Reservoir, this being the supply to Arnfield WTW, and produces 90 kWh, with the third being installed at Bottoms compensation reservoir, where a set flow has to be maintained into the River Etherow. This produces the least amount of electricity, approximately 35 kWh. Although this project is still in its infancy, credit must go to the firm of Small Hydro Projects who are based in Dumfriesshire, Scotland, for their initiative in installing and maintaining the hydro turbine units.

eight

Recreation and a Tribute

Freedom – Recreation In The Longdendale Valley

In the Longdendale valley the upper part of the hills are bleak and barren, almost wholly moorland, generally capped with peat moss and mixed with heather for the survival of the grouse. All part of the 'Dark Peak' , so termed because of the dark coloured millstone formation and shale geology and its own particular moorland vegetation which is in contrast to its descending slopes, cut into deep narrow picturesque valleys with their infinite number of streams, leading down to the shining chain of man-made lakes below, covering the bed of the important river Etherow. Until the 1970s, access around the perimeters of the Longdendale Reservoirs to the general public was very limited, with most of the 19,000 acres strictly forbidden, because there were no existing treatment plants built to ensure the water was sterilised before being fed into the aqueduct system. 'No Trespassers' signs were posted everywhere. At that time there were five reservoir keepers employed in the valley who worked 24/7, their salaries complemented by their love of the open air life and living in handsome tenanted stone cottages close to the reservoir. Among their many other duties, one of their responsibilities was to ensure the public were kept away from the reservoirs. There was an exemption to the rule at the non-drinking water compensation reservoirs where public fishing was allowed; at Bottoms Reservoir it was bait fishing, and Vale House Reservoir, fly fishing. During the permitted hours of fishing the reservoirs were patrolled by the duty reservoir keeper, who checked for possession of fishing licences; he also collected the angling fees required. It was not until the advent of water treatment plants being introduced and built at Arnfield and Godley that public access really began to be relaxed on both the drinking reservoirs and the compensation reservoirs, with more rights of way being granted to local villagers and visitors alike.

Today it is a far different scene with tourism and recreation being encouraged. It really began back in 1951, when Britain's long awaited first National Park was created. That honour was bestowed upon the Longdendale Valley and vast surrounding area in the form of the Peak District National Park. At that time this wild and stark part of the Peak was strictly forbidden to hikers, both on the 37 square miles of Bleaklow and the 15 square miles over on Kinder Scout, countryside crossed only by the worn sure-footed tracks of shepherds and their sheep with never a public footpath in sight. In 1954 the first National Park Warden Service was formed – one full-time warden and a few devoted, volunteer, part-time warden country-lovers. After painstaking work, and with the fullest co-operation from Manchester Corporation Waterworks and their tenant farmers and other various land owners, the Open Access agreement was eventually drawn up and signed in 1965. Footpath access was granted with entry from selected points along the busy A628 on the north side of the valley and the not so busy B6105 on the south side. Designated footpaths, suitably signposted, guided walkers to the summit of the open moorland. A final sign indicated 'Open Access' where the public was allowed, for the first time ever, to enjoy free access to walk and climb the open moorland without having to worry whether 'big brother' was watching.

Back in 1935, the late Tom Stephenson had a dream: 'A Long Green Trail for the enjoyment of hikers'. His dream became a reality when The Pennine Way was officially opened in 1965, bringing another triumph for town-orientated country-lovers. Flexing northwards from Edale in the Peak District National Park, The Pennine Way is routed via Torside Embankment and Crowden Youth Hostel, and travels these days over well trodden footpaths, bridleways, packhorse and drove roads, up hill and down dale, striding the rugged Pennines, the backbone of England, for a distance of 275 miles, stretching northwards to the welcoming Scottish Borders.

So what's changed? Over the years, the valley has increased its variety of recreational activities to include a private sailing club on Torside Reservoir (which began in April 1982), canoeing and windsurfing, public club-directed fishing in Bottoms Reservoir run by Medlock and Tame Angling Club, and at Valehouse Reservoir by Diggle Angling Club. Tickets are available from the

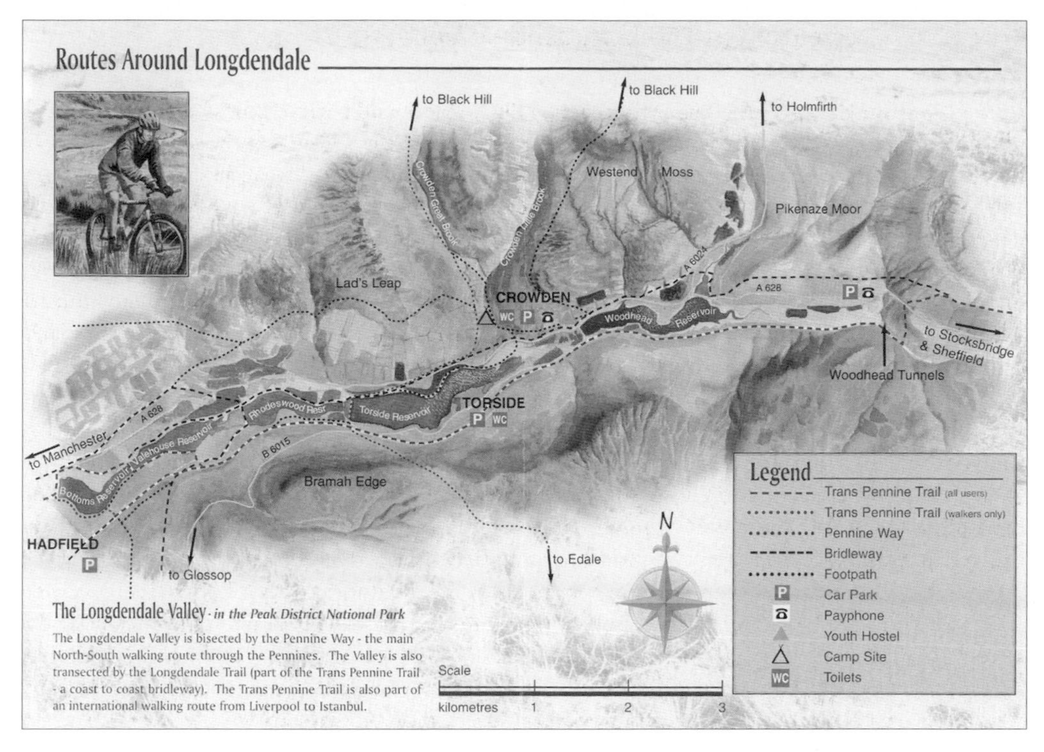

Recreational activities in the Longdendale Valley. (Artwork by kind permission of Tim Wooton)

relevant clubs. On the Longdendale Trail there is cycling and walking, embracing facilities for the disabled, and elsewhere there are three sites for climbing activities, organised by the British Mountaineering Club.

With this broadening of activities in the Park, changes were inevitable, and in 1974 the title Warden was changed to the far more suitable one of Ranger. There are now six Rangers, ably supported by over 200 part-time and volunteer Rangers, who all attend to the important task of managing this huge area, comprising some 200 miles of footpaths and bridleways alone. Rangers' duties include contingency arrangements for dealing with general emergencies, flooding, moorland fires and severe winter conditions as well as giving help and assurance to local people, visitors, youth groups and school visits; and I'll warrant, even to lost moorland souls.

Crowden Youth Hostel is near the site of the Old Crowden Hall (on page 63). The campsite, although small, provides toilets and a small car park. For motorists and their passengers this is a pleasant area to stretch the legs and take a breath of fresh air.

Torside Car Park, situated on the south side of Torside Reservoir on the B6105, provides parking facilities for 100 cars, plus an overspill car park for a further 90 cars. There are toilet facilities and a picnic area with a view northwards across Torside where you can eagle-eye the white billowing sails of the darting busy dinghies as they tack, weave, and glide across the water. The car park provides wheelchair access to Torside Reservoir and the Longdendale Trail. Unfortunately, a Visitor's Centre at the car park was closed in 2001 due to financial reasons, and the nearest location to obtain information on the Peak Park activities is the Glossop Heritage Centre located in Henry Street, alongside Norfolk Square, Glossop. Glossop Heritage Centre is well worth a visit as it provides details of many facets of local history including the eminent Longdendale and Glossop cotton mills back in the celebrated age of the cotton industry. (Heritage Centre telephone number: 01457 869176).

The Longdendale Trail is one of the latest facilities for visitors, co-ordinated by the National Park Authority, United Utilities and other interested parties. The trail's wide, hard surfaced footpath, which is capable of accepting wheelchairs, is routed along the disused Manchester to Sheffield Railway track between Hadfield and Woodhead and is ideal for cycling and horse riding the six mile length of track. From the Woodhead Tunnel the track continues over a moorland bridle path where, at the packhorse bridge at Salters Brook, walkers can observe the ruins of an inn which was once used by drivers of salt-laden packhorses on their way to Yorkshire. The Longdendale Trail forms part of the coast to coast, Trans-Pennine Trail from Liverpool to Hull and in 1996 it became an extension to Euroroute E8 which runs from Holland to Northern Turkey, some 2,000 miles!

A Visitors Survey, taken in 1995, found the vast majority of people travelled by car (over ninety per cent) and that the largest proportion came from the South Manchester and Stockport areas, with sixteen per cent belonging to local Glossop and Hadfield areas. Today, many tourists, hikers and family picnic roamers enjoy the open access to the countryside and appreciate the freedom of walking across lengths of the 275-mile long Pennine Way, with a breeze through their hair and a spring in their step. From such humble beginnings, came all this.

The Tameside Metropolitan Borough Blue Plaques scheme commemorates local people and places of historic importance. Artists, poets, botanists and war heroes are amongst those celebrated. I am glad to report that, at last, this great man, J.F. La Trobe Bateman, has been publicly recognised for his great achievements by having a Blue Plaque erected in his honour within the Tameside area.

A Tribute to a Pioneer

Right: *Photograph of John Frederick La Trobe Bateman, taken in 1882. Born 1810 – Died 1889.*

Opposite: *Honoured at Last (photograph by kind permission of the Tameside Metropolitan Borough). The plaque is located on the outside stone wall of the first and deepest air shaft of the Mottram Tunnel, being 200ft in depth (see page 24). The shafts not only supplied air for the men working in the tunnel, but they were also used for lowering men, as well as drinking water, materials and equipment, in and out of the tunnel and for removing excavated material as the tunnel was being constructed. Candle power was the only means of supplying light to the workmen and engineers of the day, and corroded remnants of candle holder brackets still remain fixed to the sides of the tunnel to remind us of that far-away age. (The location of the shaft on which the plaque is set can be seen from Lowery Court, Mottram.)*

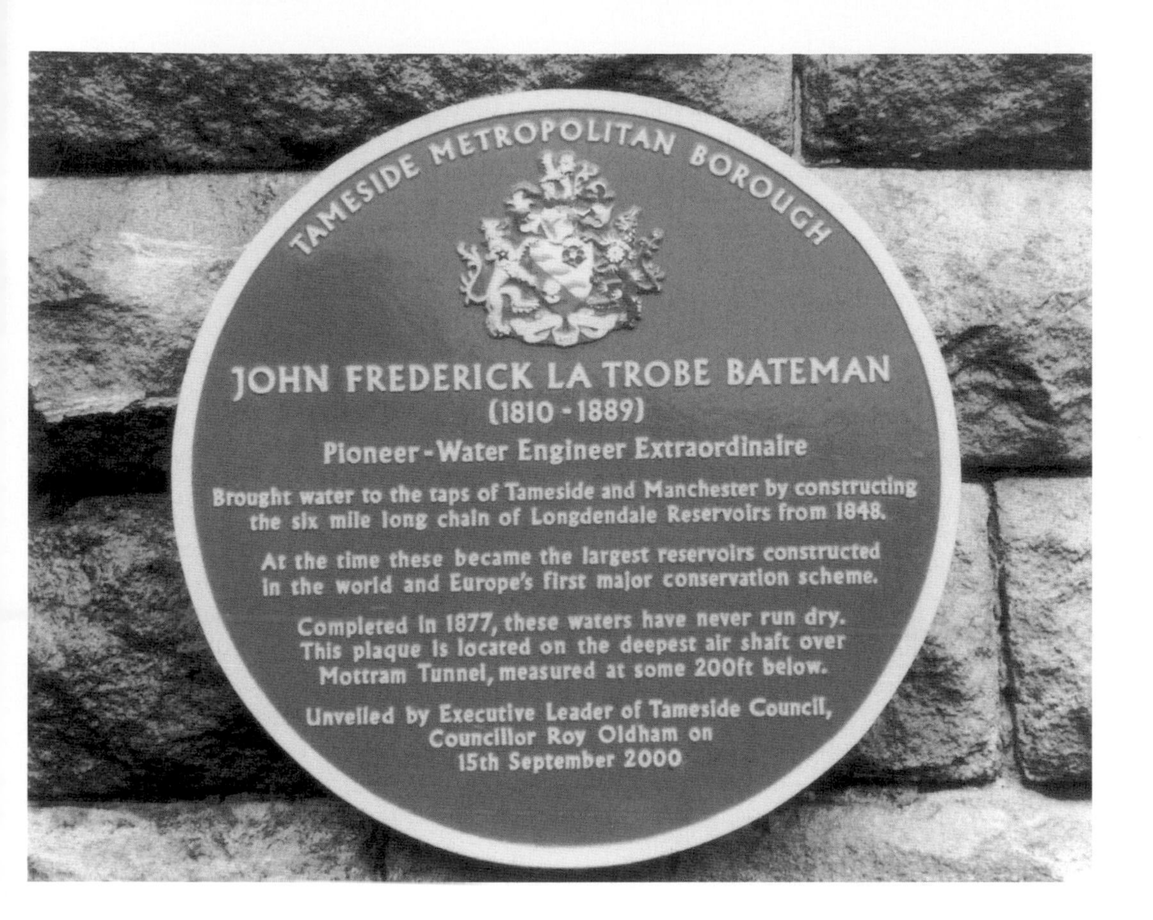

Last Words

16 September 1879

It is now many years since the last failure occurred, and though we may not expect that from time to time these weak places may be discovered, there need be no apprehension of danger nor any anxiety about the occurrence. All that need be done, on the appearance of the failure, is to draw down the water as soon as it may be convenient, in order that the place may be discovered and repaired as heretofore. I have no doubt that eventually the reservoir will remain as tight as any other.

16 March 1881

In the spring of 1877 I reported the works as finished, since which time water has repeatedly held back in both the Woodhead and Torside Reservoirs at top level.

Very heavy floods have since occurred, especially in December 1879 and in March 1880, and Mr Hill and I have frequently discussed the power of control which we possessed on such occasions.

Such is the power of water, such was the power of the man, John Frederick Bateman.

John Frederick La Trobe Bateman passed away peacefully at his beloved residence, Moor Park, Farnham, in the early morning of June 1889; he was seventy-nine years of age.

Other local titles published by Tempus

Manchester Ship Canal

CYRIL J. WOOD

In the 1880s, construction started on Britain's largest man-made inland waterway and soon sizeable ships sailed to Salford. A stunning engineering project in its own right, the 'Big Ditch' also spawned smaller wonder such as the Barton Aqueduct and it remained busy for almost a century. Now little used, it still remains a marvel of Victorian engineering.

0 7524 2811 X

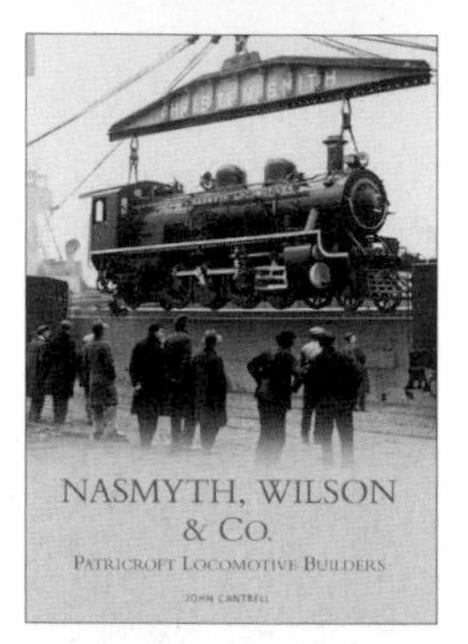

Nasmyth, Wilson & Co.

JOHN CANTRELL

Documenting the history of Nasmyth Wilson & Co. Ltd for over 100 years at their Bridgewater foundry, this illustrated collection of over 200 photographs provides a wonderful record of a valuable part of our national heritage.

John Cantrell is the editor of Maudsley and author of The Farouk Engineer, also published by Tempus.

0 7524 3465 9

The Longdendale Valley

MARGARET BUXTON

This fascinating collection of photographs of the valley over the years was selected largely from the work of Harry Buxton (1908-1983). He lived in Hadfield and worked as a local photographer for most of his life, recording people, incidents and the landscapes of his home area. He also collected and copied earlier photographs, some of which also appear here in this selection put together and described by his daughter Margaret Buxton.

0 7524 3288 5

The Duke's Cut The Bridgwater Canal

CYRIL J. WOOD

Cyril J. Wood recounts the fascinating history of the Bridgewater Canal. His detailed commentary is complemented by his descriptive guide to cruising the canal and valuable navigational information. Illustrated with over 150 images, this comprehensive history and guide will appeal to local historians and canal enthusiasts alike.

0 7524 2371 1

If you are interested in purchasing other books published by Tempus, or in case you have difficulty finding any Tempus books in your local bookshop, you can also place orders directly through our website

www.tempus-publishing.com